'If this is your i

'The handkerchief?'

'The proposal of marriage!'

'I'm deadly serious,' Josh assured her quietly. 'I need to make sure that Zoey has someone I can trust to take care of her. I need a wife to ensure that I can keep custody of Zoey. Zoey needs a surrogate mother.'

'Why me?'

'I'd rather have you around for Zoey than any other woman I know. There's a warmth, a sweetness in your nature, Annie. You've got a lot of natural love to offer a child. If you can rise above the deficiencies in our relationship, and tackle the challenge for Zoey, I'll be forever in your debt. It may not seem much of a deal, but I'll do my best to make it worth your while. The job's yours if you'll do it, Annie.'

She sat down abruptly on the rattan sofa.

'Sorry,' she said shakily, 'but I don't know what to say…'

Having abandoned her first intended career for marriage, **Rosalie Ash** spent several years as a bilingual personal assistant to the managing director of a leisure group. She now lives in Warwickshire with her husband and daughters Kate and Abby, and her lifelong enjoyment of writing has led to her career as a novelist. Her interests include languages, travel and research for her books, reading and visits to the Royal Shakespeare Theatre in nearby Stratford-upon-Avon. Other pleasures include swimming, yoga and country walks.

Recent titles by the same author:

THE TROPHY WIFE

A FRAGILE MARRIAGE

BY
ROSALIE ASH

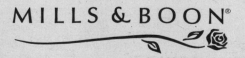

MILLS & BOON®

First published in Great Britain 1997
Harlequin Mills & Boon Limited,
Eton House, 18-24 Paradise Road, Richmond, Surrey TW9 1SR

© Rosalie Ash 1997

ISBN 0 263 80460 7

Set in Times Roman 10½ on 11¼ pt.
01-9711-54029 C1

Printed and bound in Great Britain
by Mackays of Chatham PLC, Chatham

CHAPTER ONE

ANNIE was late for the wedding.

She hurried, in fact she ran like a gazelle, down from the cliff-top road where she'd parked her car; she hated being late. She was so preoccupied, so conscious of having missed the whole church service and half an hour of the wedding reception, that she hardly registered the pleasure of being back home in Cornwall in summer, or noticed the familiar view, the blue-grey Atlantic shimmering in the hazy June sun beyond the pink sea thrift and tamarisk.

She dashed across the sloping lawns towards the marquee—long blonde hair escaping from its neat clip and flying in strands past her shoulders, short pink dress and jacket revealing an expanse of bare, tanned, enviably elongated thighs—and then she slowed down, caught her breath, composed herself.

She should at least try to give an impression of calm efficiency, she told herself disapprovingly. This might be a family wedding, but she was the proud owner of the firm in charge of the catering. She had a professional image to maintain. People would expect to see Miss Anoushka Trevellick of Party Cooks and Company looking...well, in control. Not panting for oxygen with a stitch in her side.

Halting just outside the marquee entrance, she anxiously scanned the happy throng of guests. Her own hired staff were wending their way competently through the crowds, dispensing drinks and platters of food. In the distance, she caught sight of Liv, her younger sister who was working for Party Cooks during her 'gap' year between finishing A levels and going to university, laughing and talking to Miles and Alison, the newly-weds. Everyone in sight seemed to be sipping champagne and nibbling on Annie's home-made canapés, while smiling and conducting high-volume conversations.

All in all, it looked fine. No obvious crises. Some of her panic subsided.

Did she look as much of a wreck as she felt? she wondered belatedly. Fumbling in her bag, she pulled out a small mirror and checked her appearance. A hot and bothered reflection peered back at her, but that was only to be expected. What with her car breaking down on the motorway, the long delay as she waited for the breakdown service to effect a temporary repair, then discovering that the battery of her mobile phone was flat, and the stress of running late for Miles and Alison's wedding, she was surprised she looked even halfway presentable.

She thrust a hand unsuccessfully through the wayward wisps of fringe which fell to her high cheekbones on either side of warm, vulnerable, honey-brown eyes, and snapped the mirror shut.

An unexpected wave of dizziness made her feel lightheaded. The ground beneath her feet seemed to dip, and she swayed alarmingly, blindly grabbing the nearest chairback to steady herself.

'Are you all right, Annie?'

The deep male voice behind her contained a distinctive, laid-back American drawl. Her heart lurched, then began to thud uncomfortably.

Josh Isaac.

She hadn't seen him for two years, and their last meeting had been far from friendly. But still, without looking at him, she knew his voice. For some reason, she found that extremely annoying.

Hastily she straightened to her full five feet five, and

resolved to look as laid-back and together as he did. Instead, once she'd risked meeting his blowtorch blue gaze under that mane of overlong black hair, she found herself fiddling far from confidently with the strap of her small pink suede shoulder bag.

'I'm fine, thanks. How are you, Josh?' She eyed him up and down quickly, registering over six feet of lean, athletic male. Why hadn't she realised that he'd be here? Her mother had telephoned with all the gossip about the forthcoming wedding. She hadn't mentioned Josh. But even so, knowing his close friendship with her cousin Miles, she should have put two and two together...

Last time she'd seen him, they'd been on a hot Greek island and he'd been wearing nothing but a T-shirt and frayed denim shorts. Today he was in formal grey morning suit, complete with white carnation. Her throat dried. How could she have forgotten how gorgeous he was to look at?

'I'm well enough, thanks.' He was scanning her from head to toe, with a look of concern which surprised her. 'You looked as if you were about to pass out. Are you sure you're okay?'

'I'm fine,' she insisted, summoning a bright smile. 'I just had a bad journey down from London and skipped lunch...'

'That's ironic, since I hear you're a cook now,' he mocked. 'Sit down; I'll get you some food...'

'Don't bother; really...' She was thrown by this unexpected display of caring. 'What a good thing you were hovering at the entrance ready to play the good Samaritan...'

'I'm the best man.' He grinned briefly. 'It's my job to greet late arrivals.'

Now that she came to think about it, who else would have been Miles's best man? Annie reflected, blinking uncomfortably under that lazy scrutiny. Josh and her cousin were both journalists, but she suspected that her cousin saw Josh, older and more experienced, as a role model: fearless and heroic, the war correspondent who freelanced for Reuters, ventured into the thick of war zones and relayed harrowing stories for the world to gasp and weep over.

Annie had been twenty-one when she'd first crossed paths with Josh two years ago, during that family holiday in the Greek Islands, and had initially nursed a secret crush on him. Josh had been staying at his sister's villa next door to theirs. She'd taken one look at him, lean and tanned, broad-shouldered and lean-hipped, expertly windsurfing on crystal Aegean waters, and felt a huge jolt of breathless recognition, like an emotional tidal wave, even though she'd never seen him before in her life.

There had followed an unforgettable period during which she'd gradually got to know him better; they'd hired a car and explored the tiny island, drunk ouzo on the waterfront, eaten aromatic pork souvlaki or moussaka beneath dark, starry skies. They hadn't always been alone, of course, they'd often gone out in a big family group, but somehow she'd always ended up sitting next to Josh, and she'd liked to imagine that he talked almost exclusively to her. They'd laughed and talked and talked... What about, she couldn't even remember now, except that she'd felt so drawn to him, as if she'd known him for years...

But, three weeks later, she'd gone back to England bitterly aware that Miles's idol had feet of clay...

As details of that episode filtered back into her mind, she felt all the old pain and indignation flicker back to life inside her. For a short, magical interlude she'd imagined that he might reciprocate her feelings, until he'd accused her of deliberately stealing his sister's fiancé. Condemned her as if he thought she was some kind of man-eater.

Was that how he still perceived her? she wondered wryly. If so, she might as well act in character. Perversity made her turn on her most flirtatious smile.

'If your job is greeting late arrivals, you'd better greet me properly, hadn't you, Josh, darling?' she invited, in a teasing voice. She pushed her fingers through the trails of blonde hair around her eyes, then clasped her hands behind her back, tilted up her chin, and pertly proffered a smooth golden cheek for his kiss.

He stood motionless for a few seconds, his eyes locked with hers. She saw the flicker of recognition, and knew he was remembering Greece. Silently, he lowered his gaze to the scoop neck of her dress where the swell of her breasts was visible above the pink linen fabric. By the time he slowly bent to kiss her she was trembling inwardly, and feeling hot all over.

'You think it's worth bothering with the sex kitten routine?' he teased, brushing firm lips briefly against her cheek, then drawing back to watch her through darkly narrowed eyes. 'When I witnessed the damage it caused two years ago?'

All her breath seemed to leave her lungs in a rush.

'How immature you still are, Josh,' she managed sweetly, keeping her smile glued to her lips as she caught a glimpse of Liv waving to her through the crowd. 'If you can't even manage the social niceties, you should stick to dodging bullets in one of your war-torn cities. Excuse me; I see someone I want to talk to...'

Josh's smile widened. To her surprise he caught her as she began to brush past him, preventing her escape. His lean brown fingers held her just tightly enough to trap her without actually bruising her slim upper arm below the short sleeve of her jacket.

Annie swallowed nervously. In spite of everything, it seemed that he still had an unfortunate effect on her nervous system. One touch of his hand, and all the tiny nerve-ends were delicately shimmering, like wild summer flowers in a breeze.

'You can't resist it, can you?' he mocked. 'Flirting with anything in trousers?'

He seemed to find her amusing now, she registered indignantly, unlike his reaction two years ago, which had been coldly judgemental.

'Still, I hear you've found your vocation, doing dinner parties on the London social circuit. Plenty of males to dance attendance on you? And who cares if they're already spoken for?'

This deadly verbal attack left her stunned, then quivering with outrage. The heat rose in a slow burn from her breasts, up her neck, right to the roots of her hair.

'What exactly is that supposed to mean?' she burst out, too incensed to care about the surprised heads turning their way. 'If you're implying what I think you're implying, I—'

'Annie, cool down. You're causing a scene.'

'I will not cool down! You know something? I pity you! I really do!' she responded fiercely. 'You must lead such a miserable, cynical life. With your warped ideas about other people's morals! What gives you the right to stand in judgement on me, Josh Isaac? Do you honestly think you're so perfect…?'

'Hey! What's going on here? Steady on, Annie.' Miles, brown hair ruffled, brown eyes amused, had suddenly appeared beside them. His laughing voice broke the heated tension which had engulfed them both. 'I'm a bit vague on wedding etiquette, but I'm sure the caterer's not meant to have a stand-up row with the best man. It's bad for business!'

She blinked at her cousin, some of her fury fading to remorse. Business aside, the last thing she wanted was to be the cause of any unpleasantness at Miles and Alison's wedding.

'Sorry, Miles...'

'Are you okay, Josh? Annie's verbal attacks can be as painful as a fist-fight, as I recall from our childhood...' Miles's eyes danced with teasing curiosity as he stared from one to the other, seeing the militant sparks in Annie's brown eyes and the brooding cynicism in Josh's lidded gaze.

'We're both guilty of trading insults,' Josh said drily. 'But, as you say, she's quite fierce when roused.'

Annie clenched her fists at her sides. There was a gleam in Josh's eyes, suggesting that he was milking Miles's intervention for maximum effect.

He turned his burning, lambent blue gaze on her as he added silkily, 'But maybe I underestimated you. If you're so defensive, maybe you have a conscience after all?'

With a nod to Miles, Josh turned away. He was swallowed up by the crowd just as the rest of her family materialised to hug and kiss her in turns. By the time they'd demanded to know how she was and why she was late, and congratulated her on the gorgeous food and spectacular wedding cake, her murderous feelings towards Josh Isaac and her guilt at publicly losing her temper were temporarily overshadowed by the pleasure of being back in Cornwall and seeing all the family again.

'What was all that about? With Josh, I mean?' her sister Liv demanded later. Annie had finished her lightning check on the catering arrangements, hugged and kissed the bride and groom, apologised profusely for her lateness, and she and Liv had retired to a quiet corner to continue their chat over plates of smoked salmon vol-au-vents and glasses of champagne.

'Oh, nothing much...'

'Annie, don't give me that!' Liv grinned, the same wide, generous smile as her sister's, and eyed her with scepticism. 'I'd hardly describe having a heated argument with Miles's best man in the middle of the wedding reception as "nothing much".'

'It wasn't all that heated,' Annie protested lamely. 'We just had a…a difference of opinion.'

'Really? I'm a little concerned that those assertiveness classes we went to might have had a bad effect.' Liv wound a wave of long dark hair round one finger and watched her sister with a comical frown on her forehead.

Annie carefully sipped some champagne, caught Liv's clear, patient gaze and sighed. If she had to make a public spectacle of herself, Annie reflected wryly, she could have chosen a better moment than hurling insults at a VIP guest at one of her own functions and in full view of the entire family. Even if he had insulted her first…

'Okay. He said something which made me see red. It wasn't premeditated. I lost my temper, and I feel ashamed of myself. What he said was so ridiculous, I should have laughed in his face. I shouldn't let him get to me. Let's just hope it doesn't travel too far down the grapevine and stop people from booking us for their parties…'

'It could have the opposite effect,' Liv said brightly. 'I thought it was very entertaining. So what did he say?'

'He suggested that I'd found my vocation, flirting with male clients and not caring if they were married or single!'

'What?' Liv looked so taken aback, Annie found she wanted to laugh. 'Why in the world would he say that to you?'

'Josh Isaac and I don't get on,' she explained slowly. Crumbling a vol-au-vent into pieces, she stared at her plate. 'He sees me as some kind of…well, man-stealer, as far as I can gather.'

Liv looked outraged, then puzzled. 'But why?'

'Remember a couple of years ago, at Villa Kalimaki?'

Annie pushed her messy plate away as her appetite faded.

'Vaguely.' Liv looked blank. 'Could you be more specific?'

'Josh's younger sister's fiancé, that American guy, was such a creep, don't you remember? He kept jumping on me every time Camilla turned her back. In the end I went home to England and he abandoned her and followed me.'

'Oh, good Lord, I'd forgotten all about that!'

'Josh obviously has a longer memory span.'

'But it wasn't your fault!' Liv's expression was amazed. 'If you ask me, that engagement was better off broken before the poor girl found herself shackled to him!'

'Josh blames me. He thinks I lured the wretched man away.'

'In that case, Annie, darling, you were quite right to yell at him. It's hardly your fault that you look good in a bikini! Were you supposed to come to the beach in rollers, face-mask and a baggy jumper?'

Annie met her sister's dancing eyes and burst out laughing.

'So wise, even though you're five years younger than me!'

'That was a bad year for us both, then,' Liv was reflecting. 'I had my disastrous infatuation with my perfidious Frenchman, remember? That autumn?'

'I remember.'

Liv groaned in recollection. 'I was such an idiot—the impressionable sixteen-year-old, falling for the classic older man. I cried myself to sleep for weeks, you know. But you never told me about Josh.'

'I thought you had enough to worry about.' Annie swallowed, remembering. Liv's older man had been a French teacher at their local college, who'd led Liv on then disappeared back to France without a word. Seeing bright, self-assured Liv brought so low had been almost as painful as her own experience. She'd come to the sad conclusion that falling in love was a perilous activity.

'Men…!' Annie raised a humorous eyebrow at her sister. 'A very dubious component of the human race, in my opinion.'

'I don't think the new bride over there would agree with you.' Liv smiled wistfully, nodding at Alison's curly blonde hair and radiant expression through the crowd. 'Don't you love weddings?'

'Other people's weddings are fine.' Annie grinned. 'Especially when Party Cooks get to do their catering!'

'Mercenary!' Liv giggled, eyeing her sister mock-reprovingly. 'Don't you ever think you'd like to get married?'

Annie made a face.

'In principle, I'm not anti-marriage,' she explained, shrugging. 'I just can't imagine ever getting to the point in a relationship where I'd trust a man that much. Enough to hand over my deepest feelings for him to trample on—'

She broke off as she realised that Megan, her youngest sister, had joined them. 'Hello, Meggie. You look lovely!'

'I don't, I look like a bloody milkmaid!' Meggie announced, sitting down heavily on the hard grass at the edge of the marquee. 'Peter Voss from the village just said so!'

'Not very ladylike language, Meggie, darling,' Annie teased, eyeing the bridesmaid's outfit—fussy layers of petticoats and pale blue taffeta and little white silk bib and apron—with a degree of sympathy. Miles's bride had insisted on the 'Little Bo Peep' design, and had very nearly had a rebellion on her hands when Megan, a highly sophisticated twelve-year-old, had resisted. Alison had obviously won.

'This has got to go,' Meggie continued defiantly, un-doing her apron and dropping it on the grass beside her, then unbuttoning the top of the blue dress and fanning herself ostentatiously. 'Alison's really nice, but the poor thing's got...'

'Shh, Megan!' Liv exclaimed, exchanging glances with Annie.

Annie glanced cautiously over her shoulder. Alison, resplendent in a white meringue of a dress, was at a table not too far distant, with a party of her relatives, her pretty face glowing with pleasure at somebody's remark.

'Keep your voice down, Meggie. And go over and wish Miles well on his wedding day,' Annie said lightly, bending to stroke a damp strand of honey-blonde hair from Megan's hot face. 'Alison and Miles are very much in love, and...'

'Oh, spare me the soppy lectures. You don't believe in love and marriage—you're always saying so...!' Megan pulled a disgusted face and jumped to her feet, marching away so rapidly that she crashed into Josh, who was wending his way through the crowd with a tray of drinks. The tray tipped, the glasses crashed to the ground and smashed, and a glass of chilled champagne tipped, with precision aim, down the neck of an aunt not renowned for her sense of humour. Liv gave a long, despairing groan in Annie's ear.

'That's done it,' she whispered, stifling her laughter. 'Wait for the fireworks...'

'Megan, what on earth were you doing?' Aunt Dorothy demanded furiously, having leapt to her feet with a shriek of outrage.

'Oh, gosh, I'm really sorry...'

'You've ruined my suit, you silly girl...!'

'I'm really sorry...' Megan stood there trembling, her

face flushed a deep, mortified beetroot, then she burst into tears. Annie was on her feet, about to dash to the rescue, but Liv waved her back.

'Wait, look. The best man to the rescue.'

Josh had put a protective arm around Megan, and whisked a clean white handkerchief from his pocket to dry her tears.

He murmured something inaudible to Aunt Dorothy, who appeared to calm down, then he bent to say something in Megan's ear which made her stop crying and smile shakily. He said something else which Annie couldn't catch, and which made everyone nearby laugh with relief and turn back to their tables. Two waiters came to clean up the broken glass. One of Alison's female relatives began fussily mopping at Aunt Dorothy's dress with a napkin.

'Crisis averted,' Liv murmured, her dark eyebrows arched, grey eyes bright with amusement. 'Your Josh can be rather nice, don't you think?'

'My Josh?' Annie sat down again and glared at her sister. 'Very funny!'

'I'm remembering more about that summer at the Villa Kalimaki,' Liv said. 'You two hardly took your eyes off each other. We all went out in a crowd, but I can remember how you used to have exclusive conversations between yourselves. And I can picture the way he used to look at you. Sort of hungry and protective and...proprietorial!'

'Liv, for heaven's sake!' Annie could feel herself going pink. 'Your imagination seems to have gone berserk...'

Glancing back, she saw Josh exchange a conspiratorial smile with Meggie; the two of them then vanished into the crowd. A few minutes later, Annie saw Meggie happily employed at the front of the marquee, handing

Josh the wedding telegrams while he read them out with cool humour.

Annie stayed where she was. She was disturbed by confusing impressions. He could be really kind; she remembered that aspect of his nature from the ill-fated holiday in Greece—before his sister's fiancé had turned everything sour and made Josh denounce her as a man-eater.

She'd had such a hopeless crush on him. At first he'd treated her with the preoccupied, teasing humour he used for both his sisters. Then he'd started treating her more like an equal, talking to her about his job, showing an interest in what she planned to do with her life after getting her English degree that summer...

Was Liv right? Had he really looked at her the way her sister had described? Blood rushed to the surface of her skin at the thought. She'd been so busy trying to keep her own intense emotions under control, she probably wouldn't have noticed. But the physical attraction between them had been growing, even while they'd been going around in that casual group, swimming and exploring different beaches and eating at little tavernas...

Before the faithless fiancé had arrived, Josh had been teaching her and Camilla to windsurf. Annie had been hopeless at it, and Josh had been commendably patient. One day she'd fallen off her board and cut her foot on a sharp stone in the sea, and he'd helped her to hobble up the steep steps in the hillside to the villa, picking her up and carrying her the final few hundred yards—a nerve-tingling experience she'd never quite forgotten...

She could still relive that scene—Josh in faded blue swimming Bermudas, his torso lean and tanned and athletically muscled, his thick black hair longish and wind-blown, and herself in a skimpy little yellow bikini, blood dripping from her toe.

When he'd put her down in the cool hall of the villa,

there'd been a sexual tension between them. For a time-less few seconds he'd looked down at her, and she'd held her breath, convinced that he was going to kiss her, and trembling with shy anticipation. He'd dropped his head, his eyes heavy-lidded, his fingers on the damp strands of her hair, and she'd felt the jolt of anticipation go through her like a shot of electricity; but then the inner door had opened, and her mother and Liv had appeared, and the moment had evaporated before it had even really begun.

The next day Josh had left the island for a few days, on some unexpected assignment, and by the time he'd returned Camilla's fiancé had arrived and begun his remorseless campaign in pursuit of her, and everything had changed...

Thank goodness that was all in the past, she assured herself, ignoring today's reaction to Josh with blatant self-deception. With any luck, they'd both avoid each other for the rest of the wedding reception, and then she could take care to avoid him completely in the future...

'The trouble with wedding receptions,' Josh said, confounding all her hopes by strolling over to her at the bar, half shouting over the blare of the disco music, 'is nobody knows when to finish them.'

She'd seen him walking towards her with a sinking feeling in her stomach. So much for luck, or careful avoidance. During the course of the evening he'd shed his tie and jacket, and his thick, glossy dark hair looked untidy from several sessions on the dance floor, which had been set up in the marquee, with a wide selection of female guests.

She'd got the distinct impression that he was welcomed enthusiastically into whichever group he joined. He hadn't neglected the two young bridesmaids, either.

She'd seen him dancing, loose-limbed and uninhibited, with both Megan and Miles's little sister, Affrica.

Now she cautiously recognised the olive branch, and debated whether to reject it or swallow her pride. She managed a cool half-smile in return.

'I know what you mean,' she agreed casually, her throat already sore from shouted conversations. 'If I ever get married I'll hang on for the speeches, then hop discreetly onto the next plane to the sun.'

'Greece?' he enquired, his expression bland.

She looked at him more closely, bracing herself for the attack. Was he going to stick the knife in again?

'Probably.' She shrugged. 'I'm a bit of a Grecophile. With Alexia as a mother it's hard not to be.'

'Your mother is a classics scholar, isn't she?'

She finally had the barman's attention, and requested an orange juice with ice. Josh chipped in quickly to order a cold beer.

'Yes. She teaches Latin and Greek part-time now. But she travelled all over Greece before she married.' To cover embarrassment, they were making stilted, polite, meaningless conversation, she registered with a hint of amusement.

Josh said something she couldn't hear as he turned back to her.

'Sorry...?' The music had just changed to an even louder dance track, and she was almost deafened. Coloured lights flashed on the gyrating guests on the dance floor; several older couples who'd been essaying a staid waltz or foxtrot escaped towards the bar, looking pained.

Josh caught her eye, and his quick grin made her heart flip ridiculously. She clamped down on her reaction in alarm. She was older and wiser now, she told herself quickly. She should know better than to let Josh Isaac's lethal cocktail of mockery and charm get under her guard...

'Come on...' He handed her the glass of orange juice, then took her lightly by the arm and steered her outside the marquee into the cool English summer evening.

She was so taken aback, she allowed herself to be led out without a murmur. A small silence fell when they were far enough from the marquee for the disco noise to be in the background, and for the sound of the sea at the foot of the cliff to take over.

'Have you by any chance had too much to drink?' she enquired simply, easing her arm from his grip.

'No. Unless you count a few glasses of champagne followed by an equal amount of mineral water. This is my first beer.' He took a thoughtful mouthful of the beer, and gave her a dangerous smile over the rim of the glass. 'Why? Am I slurring my words?'

'No, you sound normal enough. I just don't understand why you're suddenly behaving as if we're old friends. Or did I dream that only a few hours ago you were calling me names and questioning my morals?'

'And you weren't exactly mincing your words in reply.' There was a cautious look on his dark face. 'Okay, I'm trying to make amends.'

'You're apologising for insulting me?'

'Precisely.' He sounded wry.

'All right, I apologise too—' she kept her own voice coolly mocking as well '—but mainly because I'm ashamed of myself for losing my temper. Why the change of heart, anyway?'

His smile grew more rueful.

'I've had my ear chewed off by one of your devoted relatives,' he admitted drily.

'Liv?' Annie couldn't help laughing, even though she was finding it increasingly difficult to quell her annoyance.

He inclined his dark head slightly. It gave him a vaguely courtly air, which she found disturbingly disarming.

'She seemed of the opinion that I'd misjudged you.'

'Really? And what do you think?'

Josh shrugged. She found herself staring unwillingly at the lean muscles which moved beneath the fine white material of his shirt.

'Hard to say, unless I get to know you better,' he said blandly. His gaze moved lazily over her slender figure in the pink linen dress, lingering briefly on the golden curve of her breasts above the scoop neckline. Suddenly, she was finding it hard to breathe. She had a horrible suspicion that he was taking advantage of the situation to indulge in a cheap pick-up routine.

'Save yourself the trouble,' she said shortly, beginning to turn away.

'Annie, wait...'

He blocked her route back to the marquee, stepping hurriedly in front of her. His eyes were shadowed in the half-light, the blue gaze nonetheless curiously brilliant. Her eyes locked with his.

'Look,' he began softly, the mockery gone, 'I admit that some rather...unflattering impressions stuck in my mind after that summer in Skiathos. But your sister...'

'My sister is very sweet and loyal, but I fight my own battles, thanks.' There was a reckless glitter in Annie's brown gaze as she lifted her chin slightly, pride and indignation elaborately masked by her brilliant smile. 'I'm not so desperate for friends that I need to hold my breath for your approval!'

'I'm sure you're not,' he murmured, his voice husky with apparent amusement. 'Maybe it's the other way around tonight?'

She gave a short, disbelieving laugh. His closeness

was making her nervous. She stepped back, letting out her breath slowly, struggling to stay in control.

'I haven't seen much evidence of your being a social misfit!'

'I'm not sure discos are my thing any more,' he said drily. 'I'll be thirty this year.'

How did he manage that little-boy-lost look, at the same time as exuding a sexual aura which made her shiver all over?

'You looked quite at home on the dance floor, from what I saw.'

'Legacy of a misspent youth,' he told her, amused. 'In my late teens and early twenties I favoured a whole range of mindless pursuits. There's a bench down there. Shall we go and sit down for a while?'

He was already strolling easily in the direction of the cliff-path, one hand loosely cupping her elbow as he guided her with him. Deciding that it would look very childish to turn and run, she found herself obeying. Little shivers were running up and down her arm from his contact with her skin.

The wooden bench was positioned to take full advantage of the view of the coastline, partly shielded from the breeze by a dense screen of tamarisk. The feathery, dusky pink flowers gave off a heady scent in the dusk.

Josh sat down at one end of the bench. Annie carefully sat at the other. He cast a quick, appreciative glance over her.

'The tamarisk matches your dress,' he said lightly, his gaze dwelling with interest on the picture she presented, before he turned to gaze calmly out to sea. She watched him out of the corner of her eye as he took a long mouthful of his beer.

'So, tell me, what were these "mindless pursuits" of your misspent youth?' she ventured as the silence lengthened.

He glanced at her as if she'd surprised him out of his own thoughts. He shrugged.

'Most of them involved being too deafened to hold a conversation.' He grinned faintly. 'At the time that aspect seemed quite attractive.'

'Why?'

'If you're too deafened by loud music to talk, the chances are you'll be too deafened to think or feel.' He took another slow mouthful of beer and reflected for a few moments. 'I guess that was attractive too.'

She sipped her juice, her curiosity engaged in spite of her wariness.

'Why didn't you want to think or feel?'

'Just teenage stuff.' He pulled a wry face. 'You must know what it's like. You're not long out of your teens yourself. How old are you now? Twenty-three?'

She nodded, vaguely nettled by his tone. 'You sound as if you were rather…nihilistic as a teenager. Maybe you are still?' she joked lightly.

'What makes you say that?'

Something in his voice made her jerk her head quickly to stare at him. There was a guarded shadow in his eyes which unsettled her, made her wish that she hadn't been flippant.

'I suppose I was thinking of the job you do,' she admitted.

'Ah.' There was a harder gleam in his gaze now. 'You think what I do is nihilistic?'

'Well…you must admit there's an element of…self-destructiveness about it. Putting yourself in the firing line…'

'We don't take unnecessary risks,' he said dismissively, making the job sound peculiarly impersonal with his use of the collective 'we'. 'And, anyway, we were talking about you. From your blank expression, you obviously had an easy transition from childhood to adolescence?'

'You're quite right. I had a blissfully happy childhood, a relatively uneventful adolescence, and loving and supportive parents and family…'

'Lucky you. Quite a little Pollyanna.'

'And even if I didn't it's unlikely I'd talk about it to you!'

'Why not? I recall we talked quite a lot that summer in Skiathos.'

'I can't work out why we're having this conversation at all! We haven't seen each other for two years. We're virtual strangers now…' She was dimly aware of getting het up, of protesting too much. The trouble was, try as she might to behave like a rational adult, her old infatuation with Josh Isaac was invading every pore of her body, against her will, and against her common sense…

'We can't be virtual strangers, Annie. I taught you to windsurf. We're old acquaintants…'

She jerked her head again to see his amused expression, her blood suddenly rushing through her veins. 'Maybe. But, let's face it, we don't like each other very much!' she snapped, suddenly tense and defensive.

'True. Weird, isn't it?' He was teasing her mercilessly now. 'And yet that doesn't stop me from wanting to claim that kiss you so generously offered earlier…' He extended a lazy arm along the bench, curving his fingers around her shoulder and drawing her closer.

'Josh, I was offering a social greeting…' She wasn't sure how she managed to speak at all, her voice was so unsteady, her throat so husky. His closeness was torture. His touch on her body, however impersonal, felt like the most intimate caress. She fought for composure. This was emotional suicide. Whatever he claimed about his sobriety, he'd probably been drinking champagne since dawn. She was just a convenient challenge, his entertainment for the evening...

'A social greeting? Like this?' He moved to brush his lips over one hot cheekbone, and then the other.

'Yes...um, no...not like that...' She was shaking helplessly, overwhelmed by his closeness, trying not to meet his eyes. To her horror, he forced her to. He caught her chin in his fingers and twisted her face to his.

Who, she found herself wondering distractedly, had coined the phrase about eyes being windows of the soul? Recognising the smouldering expression in his heavy-lidded eyes, she felt something shiver and tug deep inside her.

Josh Isaac infuriated her and confused her. But, on a deeper level that had nothing to do with whether she liked or trusted him, she very badly wanted him to kiss her on the mouth. In a fraction of a second, it felt as if the last two years had vanished, and she was back in the comparative cool of that Greek villa, breathless with bewildered need, waiting for the kiss that never happened...

'Like this, then?' he murmured. His voice was thicker, deeper, huskier. With hands that felt slightly unsteady, he smoothed the wisps of pale blonde fringe from her eyes, watching her closely. She snatched a ragged breath as he moved his hand down her cheek and traced the full curve of her mouth with one long finger.

Then he pulled her closer, cradling her against him so that the heat of his body was like a fire against her breasts, and his tongue decisively parted her trembling lips and invaded her mouth to kiss her deeply and intimately...

CHAPTER TWO

THE wild reaction she felt inside took Annie by storm. Being kissed by Josh Isaac was a long-buried fantasy; she'd lost count of the nights she'd lain awake, reliving that naive, fairy-tale moment at Villa Kalimaki when she'd been sure he was about to kiss her.

Now, two years older and wiser, with her eyes tightly shut, she was swept along in a torrent of pleasure, drowning in dark delight. Her imagination hadn't done justice to the reality.

With an involuntary gasp she opened her mouth a little more, hunger for his kiss robbing her of caution. In swift response, Josh withdrew a little, and their eyes met in taut silence.

'Annie...?' His voice held such astonishment, she would have laughed if she'd been able to. Instead, with the blood coursing hectically through her veins, she was speechless with the breathtaking inevitability of it.

'Yes...?' she heard herself whisper shakily.

'Nothing...' His voice was hoarse, fire glittering in his eyes. Before she had a chance to reply, he was bending to kiss her more deeply, devouring her with his mouth, moulding her closer so that they were pressed together on the bench.

When she lifted her hands to touch his shoulders tentatively, to run her fingers instinctively through the thick dark hair at his nape, she realised how much she was trembling. Her uncertain caresses had an even more dramatic effect on Josh. His shudder of reaction made her heart thud faster. She was meltingly conscious of the male strength of his body, of the smell of him—a clean, heady blend of soap and sandalwood aftershave and warm, healthy male skin...

He crushed her even closer, slid one lean hand down her cheek, down her neck, until he was brushing the back of his knuckles slowly over the soft mounds of her upper breasts, where the golden skin was exposed at her neckline.

The intimacy sent a bewildering flame of desire through her. She shivered helplessly, her whole body weak. When he turned his hand, and slightly unsteadily slipped his fingers inside her dress to discover one tightly budded nipple, she made a small, involuntary choked sound in her throat. A piercing shaft of reaction burned all the way down her body, from her breasts to her abdomen, and lower, heating and melting in the secret centre of her femininity...

'Josh...' She whispered his name on a shaky, choked sigh and cupped his head in her hands, feeling that she could never get enough of his mouth and tongue in contact with hers.

He was stroking his hand lower, sliding his fingers exploringly over the soft hollow of her stomach, while his other hand tangled in her hair, releasing the clasp at her nape. She felt the weight of her hair tumbling loose down her back, while his caresses grew subtly hungrier.

Somewhere in the dark swirl of emotion, caution was reminding her that this was dangerous, that she was losing control. Her brain said stop, but her body was silently begging for more. Her hands moved of their own volition, down from his shoulders to trace the hard ridge of muscle through his white shirt, to explore the light sprinkle of black chest hair through the fine fabric. His heartbeat was strong and steady beneath her fingers. She could hardly breathe as the heat rose in her body.

With one slow, sensual movement, Josh's hand traced down her bare, tanned thighs, then slid with breathtaking intimacy beneath the short pink linen skirt, travelling the whole length of one silken thigh, to cup the damp heat between her legs...

Panic came to the rescue. Her eyes flew open in dismay. She wasn't ready for this, even if it was Josh Isaac who was triggering such powerful, primitive responses in her...

Feeling like a swimmer conquering the tide, she finally found the strength to save herself. She froze, pulling away, and with a sharp exhalation of breath Josh stopped. He lifted his head and let go of her abruptly.

She met his eyes in a haze of anger and indignation. His dark blue gaze was narrowed, almost unrecognisable, the pupils ink-black with desire. He was breathing jerkily. Ashamed and stunned by her hectic response, Annie wriggled quickly back to widen the space between them on the bench.

'Maybe claiming that kiss wasn't such a good idea,' he said huskily.

She felt her face beginning to burn with embarrassment, but she couldn't look away, as hard as she tried. His electric male gaze was so intently focused on her, she felt trapped in its force-field.

'You're right. It wasn't. You must have a very low opinion of me, using your cheap seduction technique...' Her voice sounded a long way away, like someone else talking.

Her fingers encountered the hairclip which Josh had undone, and she reached up to fasten it back in place; then she stood up shakily, and walked towards the edge of the cliff. She kept her back to Josh, hugging her arms round herself. The June evening was turning to dusk. The sky had the eerie colour-washed clarity of northern summer skies and the sea lay as calm as silk beneath it.

'Annie, I'm really sorry...' His voice was deep, hoarse with self-deprecating humour. She glanced over her shoulder. He looked dazed, she registered, as well as amused. The amusement spiked her temper. He had no right to find anything remotely funny about this.

'You thought I'd be easy game? So much for wanting to get to know me better! I might have known that would be a typical male euphemism! You thought I'd be the kind of female who'd be quite happy to have…have sex with you, on a public bench, in full view of anyone who cared to stroll along the cliff-path…?'

'Hey, calm down,' he said quietly, his voice taking on a harder note. 'I've taken the blame, Annie. But let's get a few things straight. I don't use a "cheap seduction technique". I don't make a habit of behaving the way I just behaved with you…'

'Neither do I!'

'Okay.' He sounded as if he was thoughtfully analysing the situation in his head. 'So we're not quite sure what happened. Let's just say that when I kissed you I wasn't expecting quite such a…conflagration.'

She winced inwardly. How could she have shown such…such enthusiasm? Annie wanted to cry. She would not cry. She battled silently for control. Slowly she turned back to look at him, her brown eyes glittering with emotion.

'What exactly is your problem, Josh?' she demanded shakily, horrified by how thick her voice sounded as she fought back tears. 'You started that. Now you're condemning me for responding? You're unbelievable. You know what I think? I think you hate women. Is that it? What happened? Did your mother abandon you when you were little or something?'

There was a short silence after her outburst.

'As a matter of fact she did,' he said drily, eyeing her with a bland lack of expression. 'But to say I hate women is way off the mark. I find that kind of psycho-babble very boring.'

'I'm sorry,' she said stiffly, her face burning. 'I didn't mean to sneer about something so personal. And I'm sorry to be boring. It's obviously just me you hate…'

'If repeated apologies were all we needed, we'd be best of friends by now,' he replied, standing up slowly and gazing down at her with an intent gaze. 'Maybe we're just…star-crossed?' He gave a fleeting grin, his teeth flashing very white in the darkness of his face. 'Destined to get our lines of communication tangled…'

'Right. So there's no point in continuing this conversation, is there?' She turned and began to walk away, on legs which felt annoyingly weak. He stopped her, grabbing her shoulders, spinning her round again.

'Annie, listen to me…' The hoarse command in his voice touched a chord, in spite of her wounded pride and confusion.

'Let go of me…'

'No. Will you just listen?' His eyes were shadowed, but held a gleam of concern. 'Are you listening? I don't hate you. I don't find you boring. And I definitely wasn't planning to try and—how did you charmingly put it?— have sex with you on a cliff-top bench. My only excuse is that you seem to have a disastrous effect on my self-control. Will you forgive me?'

'It seems there's nothing to forgive,' she managed tightly, blinking back tears, wrenching herself away. 'But since I have such a ''disastrous effect'' on you we'd better steer well clear of each other from now on, don't you agree?'

'No, I don't agree,' he told her, his voice thickening huskily. His wide mouth twitched into a smile, that disarming smile which flipped her heart over. 'And, judging by your response just now, I doubt if you're being honest.'

She was blushing furiously, hot all over with a surfeit of angry emotion. It was hard to trust him enough to believe what he was saying. Only a few hours ago he'd cynically denounced her morals. And he'd obviously spent the last two years blaming her for the Skiathos catastrophe.

'Why the hang-up?' he probed. His expression was darkly teasing as he eyed her flushed face, sliding his hands down her arms and pulling her against him. 'We're both adults; maybe it's easier for women to deny their physical responses, but can't you feel the way you're affecting me?'

He traced his fingers lightly down her backbone, then applied a subtly increased pressure at the base of her spine so that her pelvis fitted against him, and the hard maleness of his arousal was unmistakable through their clothes.

'Josh, please—don't...!' His action should have made her even angrier, but her anger had drained away, leaving her shivering with tension and bottled-up emotion. 'This isn't fair...'

'It's all right, Annie,' he assured her huskily, his lips against her hair. He hugged her to him for a few heart-stopping seconds, then slowly released her, holding her just a few inches away to scan her tense, bewildered face. The blue gaze held such lethal charm that she swallowed convulsively, her heart pounding. 'I want to see more of you.' He grinned fleetingly. 'And before you get defensive that's not meant as a *double entendre*, okay? When are you going back to London?'

'I... Tomorrow. I'll be catching the train...' He was overwhelming her, she realised faintly, completely steamrollering her with the force of his personality. Using this abrupt flare of passion between them as a weapon. She should be telling him to get lost, she should be telling him that she didn't want to see more of him, but somehow the words wouldn't come. When she was out of his potent force-field, she'd hopefully regain her normal emotional balance. But right now it felt impossible to break free of his spell…

She eased her arms away from his hold, unable to stand the shivers of electricity any longer.

Josh was frowning at her.

'The train? Didn't you drive down?'

With a sigh, she briefly explained her nightmare journey, the problems with her car.

'Liv came down ahead of me by train. We were going to drive back together. Now she's staying here a bit longer, while my car is fixed, and she'll drive it back to London. I have to get back; I've got a really busy week booked, loads of dinner parties…'

She thought of his earlier remark about her catering for dinner parties and gritted her teeth.

'Problem solved,' he said coolly, ignoring the tell-tale flash in her eyes. 'I'm leaving for London first thing in the morning. I'll drive you back.'

'There's no need; there's a perfectly good train service.'

'It's no trouble, Annie. Don't tell me you'd prefer travelling by train to the comfort of my car?'

'As a matter of fact…'

'I don't drive like a maniac, if that's what's bothering you.'

'It's not that…'

'And I'll try very hard not to pull off onto a country lane and seduce you on the back seat.'

'Josh, for heaven's sake…!' In spite of herself, she was smiling faintly now. It had got dark, without her noticing. There was a sliver of moon above the sea, throwing a thin stripe of white light on the water. The wind had got up slightly. She shivered, hugging her arms round herself.

'Are you cold?' Josh put one arm round her and propelled her gently back up the cliff-path. 'Do you want to go back to the party?'

'To be honest, I don't,' she admitted, walking slowly beside him. She wished it didn't feel so insidiously right to be strolling through the June darkness with Josh Isaac's arm round her shoulders in this proprietorial way. There were butterflies in her stomach at the thought of how vulnerable she was. Worse still, that light-headed feeling was coming back in waves. Belatedly she remembered that she'd only nibbled on one of her own vol-au-vents during the entire celebration.

'Then don't. Go to bed. I'll give your apologies to whoever's still sober enough to notice your absence.'

She laughed shakily. 'Don't tempt me, please. It's been a long day at the end of a long week and I'm tired. But I have to be around to help clear up, make sure everything's okay...'

'You look tired,' he commented coolly, inspecting her face impartially. They were nearing the lights; music and laughter drifted out of the marquee. 'You should take care of yourself better, Annie. Running your own business can be a big commitment. Watch you don't burn yourself out.'

'Thanks for the advice,' she retorted, equally coolly, 'but I don't need you to tell me how to run my business.'

'I'm just offering you a timely warning.' He spoke casually, but his eyes were serious. 'A friend of mine started her own PR company, but she didn't know how to balance her life between work and leisure.'

'Really? What does that have to do with me?' Annie snapped, annoyingly conscious of a stab of pure, primitive jealousy at the mention of this unknown female friend of Josh's.

Josh shrugged, his smile wry.

'She worked herself into the ground, had a nervous breakdown, and went bankrupt.'

'Well, thanks for the positive thinking!' she ex-claimed, with a saccharine smile. 'What's more, I hardly think that one kiss and a…a quick clinch gives you the right to interfere in my lifestyle—' She stopped abruptly as the ground seemed to dip again under her feet.

'Annie?' He caught hold of her gently, frowning down at her. 'Are you feeling dizzy again?'

'No…I'm all right.' It took every vestige of her will-power to shake herself away from his protective grip. She got a quick glimpse of the gleam of concern in his eyes and looked away.

She'd rather die right here on the spot than admit to Josh that all she'd had today was half a salmon vol-au-vent and a few glasses of champagne. Just as she'd rather die than admit to the serious cash-flow problems with the business, which were part of the reason for her working every hour God sent, with scant regard for her own health…

Thankfully the ground was behaving itself again. She took a deep breath and made a concentrated beeline for the marquee entrance. She deliberately ignored Josh as they went in, but she was acutely aware of him at her side.

'I could keep an eye on the clearing-up,' he suggested blandly. 'Presumably you've got a local firm to supply all the crockery and glasses and so on?'

'It's okay, Josh. Thanks. This is my business, and I'm quite capable of running it. Would you excuse me, please? I have things to do…'

'Sure.' His expression was darkly amused. 'Don't let me get in the way of your high-powered lifestyle.'

She was still struggling for a witty rejoinder as he strolled off to talk to someone, leaving her seething with impotent anger.

The anger was directed at herself, as well as at Josh. She didn't need Josh to point out how she might be mismanaging her life. She could do that herself. There was quite a list of lectures she deserved tonight. She hardly knew where to start.

She shouldn't skip meals when she was working, she shouldn't accept any more long-distance, family-catering invitations—at least until she'd enough spare capital to invest in a new car—and, top of the list, she told herself despairingly, she shouldn't go for lonely cliff-top walks with men she'd been idiotically, hopelessly infatuated with for years, unless she could acquit herself a great deal better than she had tonight...

At least she could stick to her guns over the lift to-morrow. She'd ring for a taxi at the crack of dawn, be at Truro station for breakfast if necessary—anything to avoid a lengthy drive up to London in Josh Isaac's car...

Annie woke to the very welcome click of a cup of tea being placed on her bedside table. She opened bleary eyes and saw her mother gazing down at her. The dark brown eyes that Annie had inherited were warmly affectionate as Alexia Trevellick indulged herself in the rare pleasure of spoiling her eldest daughter.

'Morning, darling.'

'Morning, Mum...' Annie eased herself up a little on her pillow and blinked around her. The Trevellick family home was a substantial granite rectory, just along the cliff-top from her aunt and uncle's house—Miles's family home and scene of yesterday's wedding reception. She'd been so exhausted last night that Josh had insisted on walking her the few hundred metres home, on the ridiculous pretext that she might fall over the cliff if unaccompanied. 'What time is it?'

'I've been rather naughty and let you sleep in, I'm afraid.'

Annie sat bolt upright, her heart sinking.

'Oh, no, what time is it?'

'Nine-thirty.'

'But I set the alarm… Oh, heavens, I'll miss my train…' She was scrambling out of bed, but Alexia gently pushed her back.

'Darling, I confess that I crept in and switched off your alarm.' Alexia smiled, displaying dimples beneath high cheekbones identical to Annie's. 'Don't be cross; it was Josh's idea. He said you'd told him you were catching the train, and he realised that he could give you a lift back up to London. Isn't that kind of him? So much nicer than waiting round on draughty platforms for trains that don't turn up.'

Annie hoped that her grateful smile didn't look like a grimace. She'd gone out like a light last night. Josh had obviously gone back to the party after she'd excused herself and vanished up to bed, and there he'd taken the opportunity to sneakily conspire with her mother. Of all the domineering, power-crazed…

'Oh. Well, thanks for the tea, Mum.'

'My pleasure.' Alexia perched on the edge of the bed and carefully inspected her daughter's tousled blonde hair and tense face. 'You're not home very often these days. I enjoy looking after you when you are. You're looking very thin, darling. You're not overdoing it, are you?'

'Of course not! What gave you that idea?'

'Something Josh said. Your father and I had a nightcap with him, when everyone had finally danced themselves to exhaustion and either left or gone to bed. He stayed here last night; they ran out of bedrooms at Edward and Perdita's…'

'Really?' It was no good; Annie couldn't keep the sarcastic note from her voice. Uncle Edward and Aunt Perdita were Miles's parents; their house was very large, and it had lots of bedrooms.

'So I said, Why don't you sleep here at the Rectory?

We've more than enough rooms in this rambling place to house the Fifth Regiment,' Alexia was saying, finishing up with a meaningful little smile that Annie didn't like at all. 'So you'll see him at breakfast, darling. Half an hour. Is that all right?'

'Thanks, Mum.' Annie closed her eyes, sipped her tea, and alleviated her indignation by thinking up ingenious ways to murder Josh Isaac...

Accepting the lift with Josh was now totally unavoidable. And, as she sank into the upholstered luxury of the passenger seat of his car an hour and a half later, she was honest enough to admit that as far as physical comfort was concerned it beat catching the train by quite a sizeable margin. Unfortunately, this did nothing to dampen her sense of outrage. She fumed in silence as they waved farewell to her parents and Liv and Meggie, and negotiated the lanes leading to the main road.

'Comfortable, Annie?' Josh, casually elegant this morning in cream chinos and a grey checked sports shirt, glanced across at her, his smile fleeting.

'Yes, thank you.' How could she be anything else, in a sleek, state-of-the-art Mercedes sports car, whose soft dove-grey leather interior toned tastefully with the gunmetal grey metallic bodywork?

The silence stretched on for another few miles. It was a mild, overcast morning, with rain clouds gathering out to the west. Annie thrust her fringe out of her eyes, crossed one Levi-clad leg over the other, and folded her arms defensively across the white T-shirt she wore with a navy blue sweater knotted round her neck. She gazed stubbornly ahead as they drove along winding Cornish lanes.

'Is there something bothering you?' Josh finally said. 'You're very quiet.'

The wry note in his voice told her he knew exactly how she was feeling.

'Why should anything be bothering me?' she managed sweetly. 'I couldn't possibly have any objection to the way you...you sneaked around last night, the way you ingratiated yourself with my parents, gatecrashed my house for your overnight stay, persuaded my mother to tamper with my bedside alarm...'

'Oh, that.' She caught a glimpse of his faint grin out of the corner of her eye, and seethed inwardly. 'I was only trying to help.'

'I'm sure I should be grateful.'

'Yes, you should—' he laughed suddenly, glancing at her again '—but I can see you're not. I suppose you're going to sulk all the way to London?'

She turned a cool, thoughtful gaze on him.

'I'm not a child, Josh. I don't sulk,' she informed him, with a calm she was far from feeling. 'And of course I'm grateful for the lift. It's your...your high-handed attitude I object to.'

'I was just saving you from the consequences of your own pride.' He sounded humorously unrepentant.

'There you go again!' Her calm façade was in danger of disintegrating. 'Patronising me, treating me like a...a rebellious teenager! I'm twenty-three, I run my own business, and as the eldest in my family I assure you I'm quite mature!'

'Fine. So why were you determined to martyr yourself on the train instead of accepting my perfectly reasonable offer of a lift?'

Annie stared ahead as they pulled out to pass a heavily loaded hay lorry on the narrow road. She clenched her fists at her sides.

'Really, Josh, your ego knows no bounds, does it?' she managed icily. 'Has it occurred to you that I might have preferred my own company today?'

'Do you feel so uneasy in mine?'

She felt herself blushing faintly.

'You obviously want the truth, so yes,' she admitted frankly, 'I do.'

'I'm mortified,' he said drily, his quick glance mocking. 'How can I put you at your ease, Annie?'

She was silent, suppressing a desire to scream. How could Josh Isaac make her feel at ease with him? Only by achieving the impossible; only by switching the clock back and un-saying the cruel things he'd said, she told herself with bitter humour. Whoever it was who'd claimed that words were lesser weapons than physical missiles was wrong.

Josh's condemnation of two years ago still hurt, every bit as much as yesterday's insults. She'd never forgotten that dreadful morning in Skiathos when he'd confronted her on the terrace of her villa, hard-faced with scornful condemnation, and called her an 'amoral opportunist'...

She'd never forget it. If someone you trusted and admired abruptly showed that they had no faith in your morals or motives, how did you ignore the fact?

And, now that she came to think of it, his behaviour last night on the cliff-top, whatever he'd said afterwards, had only reinforced the feeling that he held her in contempt. He'd practically seduced her, there and then, on a public footpath! Hardly a sign of deep respect.

'Well?' he queried lightly. 'Am I quite beyond redemption?'

They'd pulled onto the A30 now, and the Mercedes was silently speeding past slower traffic on the inside lane.

'I don't really know what you want, Josh,' she said crisply. 'You've made no secret of your low opinion of me. And, frankly, I couldn't care less. Just don't have the arrogance to expect me to feel relaxed in your company!'

Josh drove in silence. He said nothing for so long that she finally, reluctantly, felt compelled to risk a glance at him. His dark, rugged profile could have been carved from Cornish granite. There were lines from nose to mouth which looked deeper. His mouth was grim.

An imp of mischief made her say lightly, 'Are you going to sulk all the way to London?'

He shot her a brooding glance, but his eyes held a gleam of wry amusement.

'I wouldn't want to set you a bad example,' he taunted.

Annie caught her breath, and then, in spite of her annoyance, found herself laughing.

'Okay. Maybe we should call a truce, at least for the duration of this journey?'

He grinned briefly.

'Amendment. How about we call a truce for a bit longer? Say…until midnight tonight?' His casual tone was at odds with the look in his eyes, which was profoundly unsettling.

'Meaning?'

'Meaning that when I take you out to dinner we can manage civilised conversation.'

'That seems rather irrelevant,' she retorted slowly, 'since I'm not coming out to dinner with you.'

He didn't look at her, but she slowly turned her head to look at him, her eyes drawn to his lean, well-shaped hands, calmly negotiating the Mercedes past a convoy of heavy lorries. 'I'm out of the country on a job as of tomorrow. And I badly want to get to know you better, Annie. So have dinner with me tonight?'

She was opening her mouth to refuse when he glanced quickly across, his blue eyes heavy-lidded and dark with that lethal charm which could melt at ten paces, and added softly, 'Please?'

The rebuttal died in her throat. If she went out to dinner with him tonight she would be flying in the face of common sense, reason and self-preservation. But how could she find the strength to say no to Josh Isaac when he looked at her like that?

CHAPTER THREE

'THE food is good here.' Josh eyed Annie over the heavy green leather menu. 'Although I should think you're quite a difficult customer to please?'

'Because I cook for a living?' Laughing slightly, she scanned the sophisticated selection of dishes. The restaurant he'd brought her to was tucked away in Chelsea; it was small and exclusive, with white damask cloths, fat cream candles, huge palms and giant, trailing ivies screening the tables from each other, and soft classical music playing in the background.

She glanced at Josh through the golden halo of candlelight. 'Quite the reverse, in fact. I'm so glad that someone else has done all the hard work, I'll normally eat anything!'

'Don't you enjoy your job, Annie?' The blue gaze was curious.

'I enjoy it very much,' she assured him quickly, taking a sip of her dry Martini and laying the menu down carefully on the starched white tablecloth. 'But I appreciate the chance to eat someone else's creation.'

'I do a passable spaghetti carbonara,' he told her with a grin. 'You could come over some time and give me your professional verdict.'

She found herself laughing as she met his smiling gaze. Josh looked unfairly good tonight, she'd decided when he'd picked her up from her flat. He was wearing immaculate, pleat-front navy trousers, a collarless, open-necked white silk grandad-shirt, and a grey linen jacket. He'd confessed that he hated wearing ties, and that the owner of the restaurant they were going to turned a blind eye to this omission.

She'd reflected to herself that he could probably get away with wearing anything. He had the darkly lethal good looks and that kind of lean, athletic height that would make even baggy joggers and a sweatshirt look state-of-the-art...

'Since I adore Italian food, I'm tempted. Is that, by any chance, a variation on seeing your etchings?'

When she'd said it, she wished she hadn't. It made her think of that swamping wave of sensation she'd experienced on the cliff. She wriggled uneasily on her velvet-covered seat.

Josh was watching her across the restaurant table with a narrowed, smoky gaze.

'We don't all have one-track minds,' he teased.

The gleam of laughter faded from his eyes as he saw her frozen reaction, noted her heightened colour. 'Sorry, Annie, that wasn't meant to be offensive.'

'What was it, then?' she challenged, her gaze direct. 'It wasn't very flattering. You've still got me labelled as some kind of...sex-mad harlot, I presume?'

He closed his eyes briefly, then opened them to gaze at her, his mood suddenly unfathomable.

'It was just a joke,' he said wryly. 'For a moment there, I forgot that sex was such a contentious subject between us.'

'Because of what happened in Greece?'

And because of her naive enthusiasm last night, she added silently, not trusting herself to put that into words.

Josh said nothing for a few moments, his expression thoughtful.

'I can't deny that Skiathos was still on my mind when I first saw you again yesterday,' he admitted finally, his gaze as direct as hers. 'Whatever happened that summer, I had no right to insult you. But I apologised,' he went on with cool humour, watching her. 'I thought we'd called a truce last night?'

'So we did. But we don't exactly trust each other, do we?' She smiled mirthlessly, pleating her napkin in her lap. 'Deep down, you still suspect me of deliberately stealing Camilla's fiancé. And maybe I could be forgiven for doubting your reasons for persuading me to have dinner with you tonight.'

'Perhaps you'll enlighten me?' Josh's tone was far from encouraging.

'Well, in the light of your opinion of my morals,' she explained with exaggerated civility, 'maybe I could be forgiven for thinking you asked me out for dinner because you thought I was a good bet for a casual fling, just before you flew off to another of your war zones.'

Josh's dark face hardened. Beneath the dusky tan, he visibly blanched.

'I've never met anyone quite as prickly as you,' he said at last. 'You've got one hell of a chip on your shoulder, Miss Anoushka Trevellick.'

Whose fault is that? she was about to blurt out, then stopped herself just in time. If she admitted to Josh how deeply his condemnation had affected her, these last two years, she'd be making herself far too vulnerable.

As it was, she was bewildered by her stupidity in coming out with him tonight. She could easily have pleaded work commitments. Instead, she'd been silly enough to make special arrangements with one of her assistants, to free herself for this evening's torture session.

And she was mortified when she thought about the frantic session in her Hampstead flat, showering and washing her hair, using the expensive body lotion and perfume she'd been given by a boyfriend last Christmas, fussing with her hair and make-up, trying and discarding one outfit after another, until she'd settled for tonight's short daffodil-yellow sheath and cream silk jacket...

Old infatuations never die, she told herself bracingly, picking up the menu and fixing her gaze on the choice of dishes. But hopefully they faded away, eventually. Maybe all she had to do was give herself time to really get to know Josh Isaac, and then he'd be exposed as the unpleasant, critical, judgemental chauvinist he undoubtedly was. Or was that tantamount to opting to get to know the wolf before he decided to gobble you up?

'I'll have the Dublin Bay prawns, and the turmeric chicken with watercress sauce,' she said calmly, glancing up to find Josh watching her steadily.

'Right. We might as well order.' He sounded equally polite and impersonal, summoning the waiter with an economical movement of his hand, ordering wild mushroom soup and pheasant in Madeira for himself, and a bottle of white Bordeaux and some mineral water.

'So...' he held her gaze across the table, leaning back in his chair '...at the risk of incurring your wrath even further, Annie, what exactly did happen with Camilla's fiancé?'

She met his eyes for a long moment, then gave a choked laugh.

'I can't think why you're asking me. You've held me to blame all this time. You'll believe what you choose to believe.'

'It's a good thing one of us can take insults and criticism,' he said quietly, his mouth compressing to a hard line as he smiled mirthlessly, 'or lines of communication between us would be terminally severed by now.'

'Would that be such a bad thing?'

He expelled a long, impatient breath. The wine waiter brought their drinks, and they both waited in taut silence until their glasses were filled.

'Look,' he said carefully, when they were alone again, 'the main reason I asked you out for dinner tonight was because I wanted to get to know you better.'

'Why?'

Josh raised his eyes to the ceiling, then glared at her with a gleam of suppressed amusement.

'I don't have any sinister ulterior motive. Is it a crime to admit that I find you physically attractive? Brown-eyed blondes who look like a cross between Meg Ryan and Julia Roberts tend to appeal to me, but looks aren't everything, are they?'

'They certainly aren't,' she snapped back, her colour rising, 'and I object to being stuck in a category, like some kind of doll!'

'Sweet hell, Annie! I'm trying to be honest. Are you trying to tell me that you're not initially attracted to a man by the way he looks? If you haven't got to know him, superficial attraction is all you have to go on. Am I right?'

'Yes, but—'

'Right. If you could stop taking such quick offence, and if I could avoid putting my bloody foot in it every time I open my mouth, maybe we could even enjoy the evening?'

Annie shrugged. She gave Josh a small, wary smile. She took a deep breath.

'Do you remember what you said to me, that morning in Skiathos?'

He looked blank, then had the grace to flinch slightly.

'Whatever it was, it was spoken in the heat of the moment.' His half-smile was apologetic, with a hint of teasing. 'Was it very bad?'

'You said that I was an amoral opportunist,' she pointed out sweetly.

Josh's jaw had tightened. He drank some of his wine, his eyes not leaving her face. 'Like I said, Annie, I was pretty steamed up that morning. With hindsight, I'm well aware that I overreacted.'

'That's an understatement.'

'It was an unforgivable thing to say to you,' he conceded, his blue eyes darkening in recollection. He pulled a wry face. 'I was angry with the whole situation, for Camilla's sake. I vented my anger on you. I'm sorry, Annie.'

She lowered her eyes to her wine glass. 'Do you still want me to tell you what really happened?'

'Yes.'

She shrugged, meeting Josh's gaze with a slight grimace.

'The whole thing was so embarrassing. I can't even remember his name. Wasn't it something rather... pretentious, or outlandish? Like Pharisee or Pharaoh, or...'

'Phoenix.' Josh's hard mouth twitched slightly.

'Oh, yes. Wasn't he an actor?'

'He was a wannabe actor.' Josh gave a tight smile. 'California is full of them.'

'Well, anyway, he'd got the earring, the nose-stud, bleached his hair and used a gallon of fake tan, as I recall. And he seemed to think that he was God's gift to women. Camilla was well rid of him, believe me. Any man who can promise to marry one woman and then try to talk another woman into bed the moment his fiancée's back is turned would make a spectacularly lousy husband...'

She stopped for a moment, struggling with conflicting emotions.

'So when I saw him climbing in through your bedroom window...?' Josh's tone was expressionless.

Annie's eyes flashed sparks of indignation.

'I certainly hadn't arranged the midnight tryst you accused me of. He nearly frightened me to death. I woke up and he was in bed with me...'

'You mean he raped you?' Josh's mouth had thinned

more dramatically. He suddenly looked frighteningly grim.

'Well…' Annie sighed and shook her head. 'Theoretically I suppose you could say that's what he was trying to do. In practice, he was more like a spoiled little boy. And I got the impression he was on something.' Annie gave a short laugh. 'That was the only explanation I could find for his behaviour. I mean…I'm probably passably attractive on a good-hair day, but I don't usually have to fight off anyone else's fiancé, or husband…'

'Cocaine,' Josh said coolly.

'Sorry?'

'He was on cocaine.'

Annie stared at Josh in mounting bewilderment. 'I can't imagine why you were so upset at Phoenix's departure from your sister's life! Talk about the nightmare boyfriend…!'

'On the contrary, I was relieved to see him go. My father and older sister were secretly appalled by the engagement. Even my mother was dubious.'

'Then why the outraged big brother act?' she demanded indignantly. 'You knew what he was like, you wanted rid of him, and yet you froze me out that day as if I was the local ''good-time girl'' who'd just popped in for breakfast…!'

Josh regarded her steadily for a few moments. The long gaze had narrowed to a disturbing sapphire glitter.

'Perception isn't your strong point, is it, Annie?' he murmured at last.

'Obviously not!' she shot back, suppressing her annoyance with difficulty. 'All I know is you made me feel cheap and…dirty! What with Phoenix, and then you, that was a formative summer for me as far as men were concerned!'

His eyes darkened. As she glared at him through the

candlelight she realised that a dark flush of colour had run along his high cheekbones.

'Obviously, I behaved badly,' he conceded hoarsely. 'Let's just say that my anger over the incident wasn't motivated by brotherly feelings on Camilla's behalf, nor was it caused by Phoenix's outrageous behaviour.'

Annie went very still. Abruptly her heart had begun to beat faster. What was Josh trying to tell her? Liv's words at yesterday's reception came back to her suddenly. The way she'd described Josh's behaviour, that summer, as proprietorial...protective?

Was it possible that he'd genuinely come to care about her during those three weeks, and been hurt and disillusioned when he thought she'd chosen to jump into bed with a man like Phoenix?

Had he been jealous? She turned this possibility over in her mind, in slight shock. To cover her confusion, she starting talking again, rather too quickly.

'I was so upset for Camilla, I didn't make as much fuss as I should have done the next day. But that's why I went home early...'

'He followed you, though. Didn't he?'

Annie felt her face growing hotter.

'He turned up at the airport, caught the local flight with me to Athens,' she said flatly. 'In Athens, since he was already out of Camilla's vicinity, and no longer a guest at your villa, I felt more able to tell him precisely what I thought of him, and it finally seemed to get through. As far as I know, he flew back to Los Angeles. I never saw him again.'

Josh was silent, toying with his wine glass, his eyes lidded.

'This isn't working, is it?' she accused bitterly. 'You accused me then of leading him on. You still think I encouraged him, don't you?'

'I prefer to pass on that one,' Josh said slowly. He

lifted his eyes and raked an assessing gaze over her, from the pale blonde topknot to the flushed, high-cheekboned face, and down to the discreet swell of her breasts at the scoop neck of the yellow dress. 'The more I see of you, Annie, the more I can understand why the little jerk couldn't resist you...'

His husky words seemed to set her whole body on fire. She gazed at him in taut silence.

'What exactly are you saying?' she finally said.

'I'm prepared to believe that what happened in Greece was his problem, not yours,' Josh amended, looking grim.

'You're trying to say that I'm so...so sexually irresistible to men that they're not responsible for their actions? Don't make me laugh!' There was a hard knot of anger and frustration inside her. How could he be so infuriatingly blinkered?

Josh now seemed to be taking the mature, worldly-wise view that she obviously had slept with Phoenix, but that it was no big deal. He could handle the idea. But surely Josh must realise that she'd never, in a million years, have let Camilla's fiancé make love to her? That she would never have slept with someone on such a ridiculously short acquaintance, even if he hadn't been Camilla's fiancé...?

'You were a free agent,' he pointed out evenly. 'He was the one breaking a serious commitment.'

'That's neat. So you still believe I slept with him! What about my loyalty to Camilla?'

He stared at her, then expelled his breath slowly.

'I'm not accusing you of pre-planning the event,' he said in a harder voice. 'I accept your explanation of how Phoenix came to be climbing into your bedroom and ended up in bed with you. As far as I'm concerned, the matter's closed. I'm not sure what else you want me to say, Annie.'

There was a lump in her throat. She swallowed it furiously.

'So you're not acquitting me of the crime, you're being a man of the world and magnanimously absolving me of guilt?' she summed up, taking a reckless swig of her wine and gazing at him across the table with over-bright eyes. 'Well, what a good thing we've got that out of the way! The past is dead and buried. Let's drink to that, shall we, Josh…?'

They looked at each other silently for a long time, brilliant brown eyes locked with narrowed, smoky blue. He opened his mouth to say something when they were interrupted.

'Hello there!' Above the background murmur of their fellow diners in the restaurant, the light female voice came from behind Annie, and then its owner strolled into view.

She was a woman in her mid-twenties, and Annie decided she was probably the most beautiful woman she'd ever seen: olive skin, large green eyes and long, straight, fox-red hair. Her tall, curvy figure was emphasised by a short, clinging, silk-knit black dress.

'Josh, fancy seeing you here!' Her words were light; her eyes were anything but. The long green gaze was hot and hungry on Josh. Annie wondered why he didn't shrivel in the possessive heat.

'I could say the same for you,' Josh said casually. 'This isn't your normal stamping ground, is it?'

'You mean I should be squeezed shoulder-to-shoulder into some smoky journalists' bar? Well, I'm wining and dining a contact tonight,' she informed him huskily, managing what to Annie looked like a carefully practised lift of the eyebrows. 'I thought you'd be back on the front line in your flak jacket by now.'

'As you see, I'm not,' he said, grinning and eyeing

her up and down with an unreadable gaze. 'How are you, Veronica?'

'Oh, you know, overworked and underpaid,' she purred unoriginally. 'Journalism is such a rat race these days, don't you think, Josh?'

'True. Maybe I'll drop out of the race one of these days,' Josh murmured, glancing at Annie, his dark face wry. 'Annie, this is Veronica Whitton, chief gossip-monger on the *Daily Post*. Ronnie, this is Anoushka Trevellick.'

'Hi...' Veronica flicked her green eyes over Annie, the acute dislike in her gaze making Annie even more sure of her verdict; Veronica Whitton obviously nursed strong feelings for Josh.

Josh wore the wary look of a man who'd reclaimed his freedom after an intense relationship. Had they recently separated? Annie's imagination ran wildly over the possibilities.

She became aware that Veronica had asked her a question and was staring at her, awaiting an answer.

'I said, which paper are you with?' she repeated.

'Sorry...?' Annie blinked, even more confused.

Josh laughed. 'Not everyone in London is a journalist, Ronnie.'

The beautiful, dark-lashed eyes narrowed.

'So what do you do, Annie? Don't tell me, modelling?' There was a distinct trace of bitchiness in the woman's voice.

'I'm a cook,' Annie said flatly.

'Oh, how interesting. Hotel? School?'

'No, I run my own catering business...' With a flash of inspiration, Annie fished a Party Cooks business card out of her handbag, and calmly handed it to Veronica. 'I do dinner parties, weddings, freezer-filling—anything.'

'Thanks—' Veronica sounded singularly ungrateful,

examining the card as if it might be poisonous '—but I already have a wonderful caterer who does all my cocktail parties and so on. Which reminds me, Josh, I'm having a drinks do soon. I'll give you a ring…'

'Party Cooks could probably save you money, and provide more imaginative food.' Annie gave Veronica her brightest smile. 'Give me a ring some time.'

Veronica pointedly ignored her.

'You will try to come to my party, won't you, Josh?' There was an unmistakable hint of insistence in the redhead's voice, turning the casual question into one loaded with meaning.

'Sure, if I'm in town. See you, Ronnie.'

When she'd disappeared back to her table, Josh gave Annie a long, appreciative look.

'Sorry about that. One-nil to you, I think.' He grinned. 'Veronica wipes the floor with most of her fellow females.'

'Not just the ones she happens to find dining with you?'

'Not by any means.'

Annie couldn't help smiling back, although inside she felt knotted up with a most unpleasant sensation. The very idea of being jealous of Josh's female friends brought warning waves of panic. Of course she wasn't jealous. But Veronica Whitton had most definitely been jealous. If looks could kill, Annie would be stretched out under the table right now…

Their first courses arrived, delivered with a flourish by a young waiter. Annie, resolving to display cool unconcern about Veronica Whitton, gave the waiter a quick, flirtatious smile as he placed her prawns in front of her, and was rewarded by Josh's narrowed, grimly amused scrutiny across the table.

'Eyeing up the waiter is definitely against the rules,' he warned huskily, taking a spoonful of his soup.

'Why? You were eyeing up a fellow diner,' she pointed out sweetly, biting into one of the juicy prawns with a small surge of enjoyment. 'This is an equal opportunities country, isn't it? Is Veronica a current girlfriend or an ex?'

'An ex.'

'She still loves you.' Annie watched his face, aware that the effort of putting her opinion into words was making her stomach tight with suppressed feelings. 'Was it serious? Will you get back together, do you think?'

'I don't discuss my past love life in restaurants.'

'Why not? I had to,' she pointed out, with a small laugh. 'I don't think I've ever seen someone exude as much raw jealousy as your ex did just now.'

'Jealousy is hard to handle,' Josh agreed expressionlessly. 'She has my sympathy. I'm not unfamiliar with the emotion myself.'

There was a short silence as she tried to work out what was going on in his head.

'Do you want to talk about it?' she invited warily.

'Not really. Veronica and I were together for a while, but we ended it by mutual agreement a couple of months ago.'

'How serious was it? Did you live together?' She managed to keep her voice so light that she almost fooled herself she was happily impartial.

'No. And it just didn't work out. All we had in common was journalism. We weren't compatible.' He shot her a slight smile. 'Now, stop speculating wildly on other people's relationships and eat your meal,' he advised darkly.

Annie ate in silence for a while, her brain whirring, agonising masochistically over the bare bones of the situation. She'd always had a vivid imagination—one of the reasons she'd done well at English at school. She pictured them going out together night after night, exchanging journalist gossip over intimate meals, then Josh maybe admitting that he didn't want to be tied down, and Veronica biding her time, hiding her powerful feelings for him, plotting to get him back…

'Annie?' She jerked back to the present, to see Josh watching her with patient amusement. 'You were daydreaming again. You're supposed to make conversation with your dinner-date, remember?'

'Sorry! Mmm…I adore this food,' she said, blanking the painful images of Josh and Veronica from her mind with an immense effort, and making a careful show of eating with relish. 'Classic French-style cooking. All very rich and bad for you, but I do love it.'

'You did a cordon bleu course, didn't you?'

She took a sip of wine, and gave him a surprised look.

'Yes. Have you been following my career from afar?'

'Miles mentions you from time to time,' he explained calmly. 'I seem to remember you telling me you'd just got an English degree the summer we met?'

She nodded. 'I was planning on teaching, but then I decided the only thing I really wanted to do for a living was cook. My parents thought it was the craziest thing they'd ever heard, but they were very supportive. I'd got a small inheritance from an aunt who'd died, so I used the money to pay for the cookery course and then to set up Party Cooks.'

'And is it going well?'

She hesitated for only a split-second before she said quickly, 'I'm solvent. I confess I've had a few bad debtors recently, who've upset the cash flow, as my accountant calls it. But my client base is growing all the time. Word-of-mouth recommendation, mainly. Most of all, it's what I enjoy doing.'

'But it must be hard work.' He smiled at her faintly. 'Your mother seems worried that you're doing too much. And I'd say you seemed pretty stressed out yesterday.'

With a sigh, Annie finished the prawns and put her knife and fork together.

'Don't you start!' she laughed. 'I adore my mother but if there was nothing in her life to worry about she'd invent something. I eat well, I run and swim regularly, I take plenty of time out to go to the theatre and the cinema and see friends, and...' She stopped, her head on one side as a teasing thought struck her. 'I don't suppose you invited me out for a meal tonight because my parents asked you to check up on me?'

Josh met her mocking gaze with a flare of amused disbelief in his eyes.

'Is it so hard to believe that I just wanted to spend some time with you?' He frowned, shaking his head. 'For a very beautiful woman, you've got the lowest self-esteem I've ever come across, Annie!'

She gazed back speechlessly for a few moments, then said, 'That's not true. I have a perfectly healthy self-esteem, thanks.'

'So what's happened to you to make you so wary of men?' His question was casual, but she found his heavy-lidded gaze disturbingly intense.

'Various incidents in my life,' she hedged lightly. 'I mean, for example, seeing the way Camilla was made a fool of by a man who'd just asked her to marry him—that was quite an eye-opener. And Livvy was badly hurt when she fell in love at sixteen...'

'Fell in love?' Josh's husky voice was mocking. Annie felt her cheeks grow hotter. 'Sixteen is very young to fall in love.'

'Emotions are very intense at sixteen,' she countered coolly, 'but maybe it's different for men.'

Josh looked thoughtful.

'Maybe. Maybe not. What were you doing at sixteen, Annie? Were you falling in love?'

'No, I was too busy planning my brilliant career.' She

smiled involuntarily. 'I was a real swot. Determined to get into Cambridge.'

'Did you?'

She shook her head. 'No. I went to my second-choice university in the end.'

'Did you mind?'

'At the time, I felt disappointed. As things turned out, it was probably a good thing; I got a bit stressed over my Finals as it was. Everyone said I'd have cracked at Cambridge.'

'I doubt that. You'd have survived. You seem very resilient to me,' Josh commented thoughtfully. 'You've been resourceful enough to start and run your own business. I'd say there's nothing you couldn't do if you set your mind on it, Annie.'

'Thanks.' She met the warm gleam in his eyes with a jolt of pleasure. A compliment from Josh felt like a royal seal of approval. Annie fought down the ridiculous surge of gratitude, but she felt a renewed determination to ride out this current crisis in Party Cooks' fortunes.

There was a brief silence.

'A final word about that Skiathos incident,' Josh said abruptly. 'If you've been feeling guilty about Camilla, don't. She got over Phoenix relatively quickly. She found out that he was after her money and contacts. I think the only reason she got engaged to him was to rebel against the family. She decided she'd had a lucky escape.'

'Really?' Annie blinked at him. 'Is your sister an heiress or something?'

Josh shrugged, his smile twisting.

'Not exactly. She just has one of LA's hot-shot film producers as a mother.'

'Your mother's a film producer? I had no idea.'

'My parents are separated, but individually they're both fairly well off,' Josh said drily. 'My father—he's

English, incidentally—owns his own telecommunications company in San Diego. My mother's American.'

Their main courses came, and Annie was careful not to smile at the waiter again, ignoring the gleam in Josh's eye.

'You said last night that your mother abandoned you,' she ventured carefully.

'That's a bit dramatic,' he conceded with a wry smile. 'I stayed with my father when she left to live with another man in LA. My sisters went to live with her, and as there was a lot of bitterness over the break-up I didn't see them again for quite a while...'

'Did you choose to stay with your father?'

'Yes. He didn't handle the separation too well. I don't think he even saw trouble coming; he'd been so immersed in setting up his company, he could have been on another planet.' There was a brief glimpse of bleakness in Josh's eyes which made Annie's stomach contract in sympathy.

'How old were you?'

'Ten.' Josh handed her a steaming dish of tiny sautéd potatoes mixed with crispy bacon. 'These are good; try them.'

'You were only ten? Josh, that's awful. Ten is far too young to be without your mother,' Annie said, shocked. 'They say boys really need their mothers, don't they?'

'I survived. I guess I must have felt Dad needed some male support.' Josh switched dishes and held out the mange-tout and broccoli. 'Speaking of families, your sister Meggie is growing up fast, isn't she?' He grinned briefly. 'For a twelve-year-old she had some very adult opinions on her bridesmaid's dress.'

Something in the cool withdrawal in his eyes conveyed the message that the topic of his childhood was now closed.

While they ate the delectable meal, Josh steered the

conversation onto yesterday's wedding, Miles's new house in Camden Town, the latest mystery play they'd both seen in the West End, a political thriller by a playwright they both liked. Once they started on general, less contentious topics, they talked so easily that Annie temporarily forgot there had ever been any tension between them, even managing to shelve the underlying insult of his attitude to the episode with Phoenix...

She discovered that he'd read economics and politics at Harvard, that he had a knack of explaining the political motives behind most of the violent upheavals across the world, and that they apparently shared a liking for things as diverse as modern jazz, Mozart's violin concertos, moody French films, swimming, McDonald's fries, and pistachio ice cream, while they found ballet boring. By the time they were finishing a mouthwatering chocolate mousse and drinking strong black French coffee, Annie felt as if a time-warp had tipped her back into those three happy weeks in Skiathos, before the Phoenix fiasco, when they'd talked and talked like this, finding things in common, sharing an intense interest in each other's lives...

He met her gaze over the rim of his coffee cup, and lifted a quizzical eyebrow.

'Why the analytical study?' he queried lightly. 'Have I got chocolate on my chin?'

'No...I was just wondering how we came to be talking away so openly about ourselves, considering...'

'Considering that we don't even like each other very much?' he supplied helpfully.

'Yes.' She laughed slightly. 'Amazing, isn't it?'

'Amazing,' he agreed drily, signing the credit-card receipt beside him. He stood up, a rather dangerous gleam in his eyes. 'Shall we go?'

The London streets smelled of early summer as they walked to the car; freshly cut grass and lilac mingled with dusty wafts of exhaust. Dusk was falling, and some blackbirds were singing in the trees in a nearby square. Somehow, Annie found the evening extraordinarily enchanting. She sat in a kind of bemused reverie as Josh drove her back to her Hampstead flat.

He stopped the car outside her flat, and turned to inspect her gravely.

'Do we like each other better now, do you think? Or were we just making polite conversation?'

'I suppose I like you better than I did,' she teased grudgingly, hiding a shiver of panicky awareness. He was too close, in the confines of the car. Just looking down at the large, well-manicured brown hand nearest her, resting loosely over the handbrake, triggered those swamping sensations from last night. That shocking intimacy she'd allowed, hot on the heels of their bitter row. All those confusing feelings were overtaking her again, hitting her without warning with bewildering force.

'So, would you say that you're feeling more at ease with me, Annie?'

'Well…yes, I suppose I would…' she lied.

'Enough to risk inviting me in for a nightcap?'

She stared at him, slowly observing the dark, intelligent face, the humorous gleam in the blue eyes. Her heart seemed to flip in her chest.

'Maybe.' She smiled tremulously. 'I suppose it's the least I could do after such a lovely meal, Josh…'

His gaze grew lazier, reading her mind as he scanned her flushed face.

'You'll be quite safe, if you want to be,' he said, the wry note in his voice turning her knees to water. 'And the nightcap had better be non-alcoholic. I have to drive home and be at the airport by six in the morning.'

'Right, cocoa?' she joked.

'Cocoa sounds good.'

She flashed him a bright, confident smile, and climbed

out of the car. But as she dug around in her shoulder bag for her keys she realised that her hands were shaking.

CHAPTER FOUR

THE tension Annie was feeling as she ushered Josh into her small, open-plan flat was so strong she was sure he must be able to see it, like an aura surrounding her.

'Sit down; I'll make us that drink.' Without risking eye contact, she gestured hurriedly towards the sitting-room area. Josh, suddenly striking her as very large and dangerous, walked towards the elegant Minster fireplace and sat on one of the oatmeal-coloured sofas, moving a yellow silk cushion to the other side.

She hesitated near the kitchen area.

'Do you really want cocoa? I make very good cocoa, but I can offer tea, coffee…'

'Annie, would you please relax?' His tone was wry. She met his eyes, and saw their warm gleam of humour. Her stomach hollowed alarmingly. 'I swear I have no intention of pouncing on you…uninvited.'

She gave him an indignant look.

'I'm quite relaxed, thanks. And I'm quite sure you wouldn't stoop to anything so crass as ''pouncing''.'

He grinned at her as he leaned back, stretching his long legs out in front of him.

'I'm flattered—I think. In answer to your question, could I have coffee?'

'Of course.' Trying to recapture her dignity, she re-treated to fill the kettle. Her limed-oak kitchen was light and airy, screened from the sitting-room by a shelf unit filled with cookery books and plants. She moved around it with automatic efficiency, warming the cafetière, spooning in coffee, putting her hyacinth-blue coffee set on a wooden tray.

'Do you want any help?'

Josh's voice behind her made her nearly drop a cup. She swung round, furious with herself for feeling so self-conscious at his closeness.

'I think I can manage to rustle up coffee single-handed,' she retorted, then bit her lip as she heard the defensive note in her voice and added more politely, 'But thanks for offering.'

'Don't mention it.' He made no move to leave the kitchen. Leaning back against one of the worktops, he thrust his hands into his pockets and calmly watched her. Annie suddenly felt so hot she had to take off her jacket. She put it over the back of a chair and tried not to react to Josh's cool appraisal of her in the sleeveless, scoop-necked yellow dress.

'Do you prepare the Party Cooks stuff here?'

'Not any more. I rent a place a couple of miles away, in Camden. It's nice to have my workplace separate. I employ staff now, so there's more room. It's also easier to comply with all the health and safety regulations.'

'I can imagine. Is that why you always wear your hair up?'

She was pouring the boiling water onto the grounds, and the rich smell of fresh coffee was filling the small kitchen. She didn't look at him.

'Probably. I get into the habit for cooking, I suppose.'

'Here, let me carry that.' Josh had stepped forward to lift the tray from her hands, his eyes hooded as he waited for her to walk ahead of him. 'It suits you up. But it looks very sexy down,' he went on shamelessly, depositing the tray with a flourish on the low coffee table. He saw the flicker of reproof in her eyes, and shot her a breathtaking grin.

'Josh...' Her heart was thudding traitorously. Could he hear it?

'Sit down; I'll pour you some coffee. Do you want cream this time?'

'Please. Cream, no sugar.'

She sat down, careful to choose the sofa Josh hadn't chosen earlier. He handed her the cup and smiled down at her.

'Do you always colour co-ordinate yourself like this?' he queried solemnly. He'd poured himself black coffee, as he had in the restaurant, and now he was sitting beside her. One long, muscular thigh landed disturbingly close to her own slim legs. She found herself clenching her knees together and imperceptibly wriggling to widen the distance between them.

'I'm sorry...?' She cleared her throat.

'Last night you blended into the tamarisk on the cliff. Tonight you're camouflaged against your furnishings.' He grinned, and drank some coffee. 'You look like one of your sunflowers over there.'

He jerked his head towards the big wicker basket of dried sunflowers, their huge, cheerful heads filling the fireplace as a summer decoration. With dawning comprehension, she glanced around the room, noticing afresh the rich creamy paper on the walls, the natural, wheat-coloured coir-covered floor, the yellow silk curtains, a shade darker than the cushions and blowing in the summer breeze which was coming in at the sash window. The only contrasting colour was the bright mauve-blue supplied by the vase of irises on the window-ledge and the coffee cups on the tray.

'I see what you mean. Needless to say, the tamarisk was coincidence,' she told him gravely, 'but I suppose I do like creams and shades of yellow. They make the place feel as if the sun's shining, even when it's not...'

'I need the sun too.' Josh stretched his long legs out again, looking very much at home beside her. 'What's the betting we both have summer birthdays?'

'End of August.' She sipped her coffee, relaxing a little. 'How about you?'

'Early June. That proves the theory. If you're born in summer you have less tolerance for the winter.'

'I'm sure you made that up.'

'I did.'

She started laughing, then glanced across to find his eyes kindling with a darker gleam of appreciation. It was too late to switch back into wary watchfulness.

'You're beautiful when you're angry,' Josh murmured, 'but when you laugh you take my breath away, Annie.'

Suddenly the yellow sheath dress seemed far too small and skimpy, the neckline cut much too low, the skirt much too short. She felt her breasts tighten, even her nipples contracting at the hint of suppressed desire in his voice.

With a last-ditch effort to stay in control, she tried to stare at him objectively, to analyse his face properly, to discover what it was about him that was so devastating to her common sense.

He wasn't even conventionally handsome, she told herself determinedly; all right, he had that thick black hair, worn a little too long for a regular office job, and dark olive skin and those heavy-lidded, sensual, smoky-blue eyes, but his face was too angular, his features were too large, his nose too long, his mouth too wide. All in all he had a world-weary appearance, undeniably tough and male and vaguely dangerous, but which didn't begin to explain this alarming effect on her powers of self-preservation...

'Don't look so reticent; I'm not about to take unfair advantage of a lone female in her flat.'

'I should hope not,' she joked lightly, acutely self-conscious. She stood up quickly, intending to pour more coffee, tripped over Josh's outstretched legs and toppled neatly into his lap, her face burning at the abrupt dose of close body contact, far too near to Josh's laughing blue eyes for peace of mind…

'On the other hand, if you insist,' he drawled softly, closing his arms round her gently. 'Come to think of it, Annie, I'm just dying to know how it feels to kiss a sunflower…'

Annie stopped struggling to get up and went very still. He put a finger under her chin and raised her hot face to his. He smiled into her eyes.

'Annie?' His husky question was breathed inches from her face. 'Are you afraid of me?'

She stared back, her pulses thundering, her eyes wide as she gazed at him. She wasn't afraid of Josh, exactly. She was afraid of where her own desperate attraction to him might lead. But she felt almost faint with longing.

She tried to speak and found that her voice had deserted her. The look in Josh's eyes had changed drastically, from teasing to dark, brooding intensity.

'Annie…' His voice was a husky groan. 'Oh, hell, I've been trying to keep my hands off you all night…'

He bent his head and kissed her, his mouth moving with gentle hunger on hers, triggering responses she had no way of resisting. She was pitched into that same alarming lassitude she'd experienced last night. She closed her eyes and opened her lips to him, and kissed him back with a shy hunger that seemed to fuel the heat between them.

Abruptly, the heat became a fire. She was dimly aware of the shudder of reaction which went through Josh's body. The change was subtle but overwhelming—the power of his desire ignited something in her which made her whole body tremble with answering need.

'Annie…sweetheart…' His mouth was finding the delicate hollows in her neck, where her pulses throbbed unbearably, and she shivered with agonised emotion. 'I want you. I think you know that. I've thought about making love to you for so long... I wanted you two years ago...' The hoarse words were interspersed with light, hungry, sensual kisses which demolished her resistance, his eyes moving over the soft swell of her breasts. 'I wanted you then. And I have to admit I've thought about it ever since...'

'Me too...' she heard herself whisper helplessly. Her cheeks were hot.

'You have...?'

'Yes,' she heard herself admitting idiotically, wishing she could find the strength to lie to him. 'That is, I mean...I've thought about it, on and off, but...oh, Lord, I'm so hot...'

The rush of heat suffused her whole body as the dangerous intimacy of the situation abruptly descended on her. Josh's gaze dropped to her flushed neck and breasts at the scoop neckline of her dress. His crooked smile made her bones melt.

'There's a simple, short-term solution to that,' he teased huskily, and he reached round to unzip her dress. She could hardly breathe as he peeled the yellow cotton, with slightly unsteady hands, down to her waist.

The boldness of his action left her trembling and unsure of herself. And then she was mesmerised, like a rabbit dazzled by headlights, watching the sudden tautness in his face, the darkly lidded gaze moving over the soft mounds of her breasts in their white lace covering. Her nipples were tight with electric sensations that zigzagged through her nervous system.

'You're exquisite,' he breathed, lifting his hands to her face. 'Irresistible...' His smile took her breath away again as he crushed her closer in his arms. 'I want to kiss every sweet, soft, edible inch of you...'

'I'm not edible...' she whispered on a choked laugh. Mingled with the helpless shivers of desire was the knowledge that this was madness, that she was crazy, letting this happen with Josh; it was too fast, too soon…

'Aren't you?' he teased darkly. He reached first to unclip her hair, running his fingers through the heavy blonde mass which tumbled down, and then to unfasten the wisp of lace covering her breasts, bending his head to suckle one rosy nipple with slow, tantalising skill.

Indescribable reactions skittered through her. Her stomach was melting, thought Annie wildly; her whole body was melting too. Was it physically possible to dissolve into a pool of warm honey? Blindly, she felt herself pushed sideways onto the soft cushions of the sofa, felt Josh's long, hard body trapping her beneath him, and found herself clutching his head to her breast with trembling fingers, her head spinning with the delicious sensations he was creating inside her. The flushed feeling had spread all over, like a fire simmering just beneath the surface of her skin.

'I feel so hot, I can hardly breathe…' she whispered unsteadily.

'You're still wearing too many clothes,' he teased thickly. 'That's why…' With fierce tenderness he scooped the dress down over her hips, leaving only her white lace panties guarding her modesty. With swift impatience he tore off his own jacket and shirt and tossed them to the floor, his heavy-lidded eyes not leaving her face. Her heart was thudding so violently, she could hear it echoing through her bloodstream. She was on fire; she couldn't think straight any more.

As if in a dream, she let her hands move of their own volition, to explore the lean strength of his chest, stroke the rougher patch of black hair between the flat brown nipples. His body felt warm and strong, the muscles loose-knit and athletic, vibrantly alive beneath her fingers. With shy intensity, she caressed him; she encountered two indented scars on his right shoulder, and her fingers lingered over them questioningly.

'War wounds,' he murmured against her hair. 'Proof that I've got nine lives. Or proof that I'm far from perfect...'

'Nobody's perfect,' she assured him in a choked voice, a shudder of emotion making her clasp him tighter in her arms, 'but I think you're the most beautiful man I've ever seen...'

He lifted his head then, slowly, to look at her, tousled black hair partly obscuring his face, his gaze profoundly enigmatic as he searched deep into her blank, unfocused eyes.

'Annie...darling Annie...' His whole body seemed to shudder with urgency. With his mouth and hands and body, he began a fierce, hungry, sustained assault on her senses until Annie was so aroused, so utterly vanquished by her need for him, the last, small, niggling voice of reason had to fight its way through layers of desire, until it was almost too late.

But when Josh reached to slide her panties down over her hips, finally dispensed with his own remaining clothes, and she tremblingly registered the dark male power and size of his body, the alarm bells rang loud and clear in her head. With a rush of awareness, the stark irony of the situation reasserted itself.

Think, Annie, think! she lashed herself. Josh thought she was experienced. Josh thought she'd slept with Phoenix. Whereas in cold reality, to date, far from indulging in a casual, meaningless night of sex with another girl's fiancé, she had never slept with anyone at all. The gulf between Josh's perception of her, and the truth was so great it was hopeless.

No matter how much she wanted to, she couldn't let this happen, she realised with a choked feeling of panic. She couldn't let Josh be her first lover. She'd always vowed to herself that this momentous event would be with a man who loved her. Josh didn't love her. Josh, for all his devastating effect on her defences, actually had a pretty low opinion of her.

He was hard and warm against her soft nakedness, his hair-roughened body moving to pin her to the sofa. Through the haze of numbing desire, she gave a low groan, caught his hand as he stroked his fingers down over her stomach. He seemed to mistake her meaning; maybe he thought she was guiding his hand to another pleasure zone, because he raked his other hand into her hair, and sought her mouth with his. She panicked. She began to fight him, with unnecessary wildness, and he stopped then, almost immediately, releasing her slowly, searching her hot face with passion-dark eyes.

'Annie? What is it, sweetheart?'

'I…I can't… Please stop…' She was staring at him with pleading eyes, shaking all over, almost as if she had a fever. 'I'm sorry…'

The silence was almost tangible.

Josh shifted slowly, easing the pressure on her, taking his muscular weight on his forearms. Beads of sweat glistened on his forehead, and on the muscles of his chest. His breathing was ragged.

'No, it's me who should be sorry. I guess I misjudged things…' he managed thickly.

She was going hot and cold in turn, the flare of panic giving way to an acute sense of humiliation and embarrassment. She felt her heart contract so painfully that she had to bite her lip to stop herself from bursting into tears. She'd made a fool of herself, and now she had no idea how to retrieve the situation.

'I feel such an idiot…' she whispered miserably.

'It's a woman's prerogative to change her mind,' he said quietly. He moved to lie beside her on the sofa, one arm round her still, but restraint showing in every line of his body. His dark gaze was brooding on her flushed, dazed face. 'However…it would have been preferable if you'd said no a little earlier, Annie.'

She managed to sit up slightly, her flush spreading from her face down onto her neck and chest.

She attempted a small laugh. 'I should have mentioned it while I was serving the coffee, shouldn't I? Black or white? Oh, and by the way, I'm not planning on having casual sex with you tonight.'

His face darkened, even though he smiled slightly.

'You know what I meant.'

'Well, yes…' She swallowed, a hard lump forming in her throat. 'I'm not sure why I let things go that far, Josh. I just wasn't thinking straight.'

Her small voice of distress seemed to cut through his cool reserve. With a soft curse, he pulled her into his arms and held her rigid body against him, one hand stroking her hair. She was appalled at herself for starting to cry. Hot tears soaked her face and his chest.

'It's okay, Annie.' His laugh was rueful. 'Hell, every time I get together with you things go wrong,' he admitted huskily, putting her away from him a fraction to inspect her flushed, tear-streaked face. 'God knows why. I don't have such a serious communication problem with other people…'

'Other women, you mean? I'm sure you don't…' she managed in a muffled voice.

A shrill beeping sound came from the pile of clothes scattered at their feet. Josh cursed softly and fiercely under his breath and swung his long legs down to the floor. A rapid swoop on his jacket produced a mobile phone.

Clutching her arms shakily round her breasts, Annie watched numbly as he stabbed a button and snapped out his name. The monosyllabic conversation lasted less than twenty seconds before he thrust the phone back in his jacket pocket. He began coolly reaching for his clothes. She snatched up her dress to cover her own nakedness, dying slowly inside. He said nothing until he was fully dressed, a bleak, preoccupied look in his eyes as he gazed down at her.

'Don't tell me,' she joked, to hide her anguish. 'One of your other women? Are you expected somewhere else tonight, Josh?'

Veronica's, maybe? she thought, but didn't say it.

'There's a big story breaking in Bosnia,' he told her bleakly. 'One of my colleagues has gone missing. They've booked me on an earlier flight.'

'Oh, Josh, I'm sorry…' She bit her lip, hating herself for her flippancy.

'I've got to go. I'm sorry to walk out on you so abruptly, Annie.' He hesitated, then added quietly, 'I'll ring you. As soon as I get back.'

'What for?'

'To discuss my…villainous behaviour?' He sounded wearily amused suddenly, as if the black humour of the situation had just hit him. 'When you said you weren't thinking straight, that makes two of us. I was acting out of character tonight. I don't usually expect women to sleep with me on a first dinner date. I'll ring you, okay?''

She felt her stomach clench with fresh humiliation. She flushed hotly. So that *was* what he'd expected from her all along. Based on the behaviour he imagined he'd witnessed in Skiathos, he'd assumed she'd be happy to have sex with him tonight. She'd had misgivings about going out for dinner with him right from the start…it sounded as if she'd have been wise to heed her own warning signals…

'It's all right, Josh.' Her eyes were over-bright as she gazed up at him. She spoke politely, arranging her face into what she hoped was an expression of cool indifference. 'I really do hope your colleague is all right.

And…good luck on the trip. But you needn't feel you've got to bother ringing,' she added with dignity. 'I'm obviously a bit naive, but I think I'm beginning to understand what was going on tonight. I'm well aware of your opinion of me.'

'Annie, damn it to hell, you're the most infuriating female…' He thrust a furious hand through his hair, glaring at her with such suppressed rage that she flinched back slightly against the cushions. 'You have a real talent for misinterpretation, you know that?'

'Obviously,' she agreed tonelessly. 'That's how I came to misinterpret your motives tonight.'

'Annie…'

'Oh…just go. Please go,' she whispered desperately, her pretence at calm composure deserting her. 'Just go, Josh!'

He expelled his breath sharply. Then he grabbed his jacket, and strode out of the flat without another word.

It was a long, long time before Annie found the strength to move from her crouched, frozen foetal position on the sofa, and then it was only to crawl into bed and hide, with the covers pulled over her head.

'Telephone for you, Annie.'

Liv's voice floated through to Annie as she stood under the shower. She was shampooing her hair and lathering her body with a generous quantity of vanilla-scented shower gel. As usual, the message that someone was on the phone brought a shudder of fierce apprehension. Since the phone rang frequently and a whole week had elapsed with no word from Josh, she was beginning to feel under permanent emotional siege.

It had been an exceptionally busy week, though, which had helped. At least she'd been able to bury herself in her job, get the satisfaction of creating delicious new recipes and of seeing happy people enjoying their dinner parties or anniversary functions because of her efforts.

She might be in the habit of messing up her love life, she thought ruefully, but she could claim modest success in her working life.

But even that was hardly plain sailing at the moment. There'd been a series of irritating problems over the past few days, making her job harder than it should be. Liv had driven up from Cornwall in her car, only to break down again five miles from the flat. A power-cut had ruined a freezer-load of food at her rented kitchen in Camden. One of her part-timers had let her down at the last minute, which meant she'd been short-staffed at an important party. More bills had arrived, to pile up balefully in her office. And, in the stress of it all, she'd made a couple of silly blunders which she winced to recall…

'Who is it?'

'Josh.'

Her throat dried. Her heart stopped, leaped, then crashed into painful thudding. Resolutely, she carried on shampooing.

'Tell him I'm not here.'

'No way! I've already said I'd fetch you. He's calling long-distance, so you'd better hurry…'

Annie switched off the shower, and slid the shower screen a fraction. Her sister stood there with a determinedly encouraging look on her face which made Annie want to scream.

'Please, Liv? Do me this one favour…'

'You've been like a cat on hot bricks waiting for him to ring! Talk to him, for pity's sake, Annie,' Liv advised, helpfully fetching a large white towelling robe from the peg on the back of the door and waving it in front of her.

Clutching the robe round her, Annie gave Liv a reproachful glare, then went slowly to the telephone in the kitchen. With any luck, he'd have rung off. Calling long-distance? Did that mean he was ringing her from some battlefield in Bosnia? With a hollow stomach, she picked up the receiver.

'Yes?'

'Annie? You took your time.' Josh's voice sounded strange—distant and muffled. 'I haven't got long; I just wanted to—'

'Where are you ringing from?' she cut in coolly. Her stomach was in knots, her heart crashing against her ribs.

'What? Paris. Listen, Annie…'

So he wasn't calling from some dangerous front-line position, dotted around with land-mines… The knowledge gave her courage.

'I don't want to know, Josh. I said not to ring. I meant it. I have to go now…' It took such an effort to refuse him, she was shaking all over.

'Annie, don't hang up…' He sounded strained, as if he really wanted to yell at her but was exercising self-control. He had commendable quantities of self-control, she recalled, wincing as memories of last week's humiliation plunged her into fresh misery. She was blushing again as the images fought to the surface.

'Sorry, but we've nothing to talk about, Josh…'

'Annie!' The fierce insistence in his voice made her heart flip in her chest. Just for a rash instant, she allowed herself to wonder if he sounded genuine, if he really wanted to see her again to sort things out… She went very still as he continued urgently, 'I'm just ringing to let you know that I'll be tied up abroad for the foreseeable future. Something has happened that's going to take up my whole attention for a while…'

The misery which had lightened for a few seconds crashed back down on her like a lead weight. Fine, he was giving her the polite brush-off. Why he needed to ring her to do that, heaven only knew. A belated sense of honour, maybe. Somehow, it felt more insulting than the kind of silence which spoke volumes at the end of a relationship...

'Why are you telling me this?' she asked coolly. 'You're a free agent, Josh. You can do what you want. Anyway, I must go. I was in the shower getting ready to go out; I've...I've got a date.'

Cutting him short in mid-protest, she dropped the receiver shakily back on the hook and stared at it, rather as she would at a snake in a basket. The 'date' was fabrication—to describe a platonic evening out with Derrick Butterford as a 'date' was definitely inappropriate. He was a junior partner with the firm of accountants she used for Party Cooks. She saw him very casually when he suggested a theatre trip, or the occasional Italian meal.

She was still trembling, she registered vaguely. Hardly aware of Liv coming up behind her, she jumped as if she'd been shot when the telephone rang again. Grabbing it, she yelled furiously, 'Are you deaf, Josh? We have nothing to say to each other,' only to hear the mildly startled tones of her mother's voice at the end of the line.

'Anoushka? Is that you? Are you all right, darling?'

Annie sighed, meeting Liv's dancing eyes with a grimace of despair.

'Sorry, Mum. I...I thought you were someone else.'

'Evidently. Lucky I wasn't your best customer,' murmured Alexia. 'Are you by any chance having problems with your love life, darling?'

'Not at all. I don't have one,' Annie assured her coldly. 'Did you want to speak to me or Olivia?'

Her mother hesitated.

'Well, in the circumstances, maybe you could put Olivia on?'

'Right. And...um...sorry. I didn't mean to be rude...'

'Don't worry, dear. You need a break, that's all. You've been working too hard; I knew it all along. That charming man Josh who was here after the wedding thought so too. I've been talking it over with your father, and we both think...'

Speechlessly, Annie held the receiver at arm's length until Liv took it, then made a dignified retreat to her bedroom. She was too agitated to cry, too indignant to get dressed. Liv found her sitting on her bed, her knees drawn up to her chin, her arms wrapped tightly round them, staring out of the window at the trees on the Heath.

'You can't go on like this, Annie, love...'

Annie settled a round-eyed gaze on Liv, seething with amazed resentment. 'What do you mean, exactly?'

'Fretting yourself into a state of near exhaustion,' Liv explained levelly, coming to slip an arm around her sister as she sat beside her on the bed. 'Even before this Josh thing you were overdoing it, running yourself ragged, trying to do everything yourself. But this last week, well, admit it, Annie. One important luncheon party where we completely forgot the first course...'

'Not ''we'',' Annie corrected her staunchly. 'I forgot the first course...'

'Well, yes, you forgot the first course.'

'At least I thought on my feet. I've never prepared twelve lemon soles with prawns and wild mushrooms from scratch quite as fast in my life,' Annie recalled, with a slight shudder.

'True. But then you absent-mindedly wiped an entire file of customer details from the computer...'

'Okay.' Annie held up a hand, meeting her sister's gaze in resignation. 'Nobody's perfect. I admit I'm feeling a little...out of control. So what's the verdict from the family council meeting?' she finished up with sarcasm.

'Greece,' Liv said without preamble. 'Mum and Dad are sending you the air ticket. They want you to take a week's break at the villa, and I agree.'

'But I can't just leave the business! Especially not now, Liv! According to Derrick, we could be on the verge of bankruptcy!'

'I'm sure Derrick exaggerates to create more business for his practice,' Liv stated confidently, 'and you *can* leave the business, Annie. I can cope, with a little help from family and friends. There's nothing you can do about the money problems, apart from take a break to get your own act together. That could be the best tonic Party Cooks could receive!'

'Thanks a lot! It's not very flattering to hear that everyone is so keen to get rid of me, Livvy!'

'Seriously, love, nobody cooks quite like you do, but Mum's offered to come up and take over for the week.' Liv grinned. 'Dad's knee-deep in writing one of his theology ''best-sellers''; he won't even notice she's gone. And even you can't fault her cooking!'

'I wouldn't dare, but, even so, it's my business, Liv! I can't afford to take time off right now...'

'Your friend Susan said she'd lend a hand. Just a week,' Liv said coaxingly. 'Think about it—total peace, relaxing under the pines on a sunny beach, swimming in the calm blue Aegean, eating Greek salads and sipping retsina on the terrace, meditating...'

'I hate retsina.'

'Sipping dry white wine on the terrace,' Liv amended, unruffled. 'The nights will still be cool enough to sleep through, and the tourists won't have arrived in force. You can recharge your batteries and come back refreshed, invigorated. You'll be tanned, relaxed, a new woman. And you'll have had valuable experience of delegation, something which you're not all that hot on...'

'Liv...?'

'Mmm...?'

'Shut up.' Annie managed a rueful laugh, and did her best at some positive thinking. She stared out of the window for a long time, mulling things over in her head. She distractedly chewed a fingernail, a habit she'd kicked years ago. Finally, she looked back at her sister with a long, shuddering sigh.

'I'm insulted but I'm tempted,' she said frankly. 'If I'm honest, if I don't get away for a bit I might put sugar in the potatoes and salt in the chocolate mousse, and that wouldn't be good for business either...'

'Brilliant! You won't regret it, Annie...'

'Hang on...' Annie shot her sister a warning glance. 'I think you and Mum are being impossibly interfering and bossy, but I appreciate your concern and I'll think it over and let you know...'

'That's settled, then.' Liv beamed happily, jumping off the bed and making a beeline for the wardrobe. 'I'll help you pack.'

CHAPTER FIVE

VILLA KALIMAKI stood on a thickly wooded promontory. Its white walls and arches were thick enough to deflect the midday sun, and its vine-shaded terrace overlooked the sea, three hundred steps down the dusty, olive-covered hillside.

Annie knew there were three hundred steps; she and Liv had counted them, years ago. They'd debated as to whether the architect had deliberately chosen that number, or if they'd been constructed at random. She'd been here so often during her childhood, it was like a home from home. And Mum and Liv had been right; its immediate effect was to relax and refresh. There was something about the lazy pace of Greek island life that put problems in perspective. By the end of her first full day, she felt as if she'd been there a month.

She'd spent the day swimming and sunbathing. Now, stretched out on a sun-chair on the terrace, she gazed through trailing curtains of purple bougainvillea and scarlet hibiscus, and watched the boats slicing through the water far below. It was too hot to eat. She'd fixed herself a lazy snack of bread, feta cheese, olives and tomatoes, with a glass of crisp, dry white wine, and surrendered to the hedonistic pleasure of doing absolutely nothing apart from reading the paperback thriller she'd bought at the airport.

Deciding, eventually, that a little gentle exercise could do her nothing but good, she stood up slowly, stretching luxuriously in her green and cream striped shorts and tiny green crop-top, pushed her bare feet into espadrilles, and set off unhurriedly to make the descent to the beach.

The sun was lower in the sky and the heat of the day was fading a little. The smell of the olive trees, with a scattering of pine and juniper thrown in, was a fragrance which took her straight back to those happy childhood days, counting the steps. And, she registered unwillingly, to that ill-fated holiday when Josh had helped her back up to the villa after her windsurfing accident...

She wouldn't think about that. She was much too fond of Skiathos, and of Villa Kalimaki, to let disturbing memories from the past colour her enjoyment. And, if she concentrated on the small details of the present, on the stretching feel of thigh and calf muscles on each downward step, on the soft scuff of her feet against the uneven stone, the shrill of the cicadas, and the distant drone of a passing boat, she could block out everything but the intense pleasure of the moment. She made a satisfactory mental comparison between this and the cacophony of a London evening, and felt the small glow of pleasure intensify with each minute that passed.

The beach was deserted, which wasn't unusual. It was accessible only to the private villas, or by boat. During the day, even at the height of the season, it got only a handful of visitors. By evening, it was usually quiet again.

Loving the solitude, Annie wandered down to the sea, sat down on the warm sand, and watched the ripple of small waves at the crystal-clear water's edge. She enjoyed being by herself. If she felt like some company tonight, she'd drive down to Dimitri's taverna and treat herself to a meal out. She'd known Dimitri and his family for years; she'd be afforded protection there from the roving male *kamakia* or 'harpoonists', as they were known, fishing for lone foreign women.

A muffled cry in the distance made her twist round, unsure at first if it was a bird's cry or a child's. A flash of movement among the trees halfway down the hill caught her eye, and, as she strained to see, she realised that a small figure in red was running at full tilt down the hillside. Surprised, she watched the child's hectic progress towards the beach, and rose slowly to her feet, frowning slightly.

It was a small girl, of perhaps no more than three or four, Annie guessed. She was wearing a short red-striped dress and she carried a small dark brown teddy bear under her arm, which wore a matching red dress. And she was crying, Annie registered, with a pang of genuine alarm. She ran straight past Annie, gasping for breath, stopping only when her bare feet hit the shallow water, where she lost her balance, sat down abruptly and cried even harder.

Annie glanced quickly round, expecting an adult to appear at any moment in hot pursuit. When no one came, she went carefully into the water, and crouched down beside the child.

'Hello, can I help? Where are your mummy and daddy?'

The crying continued, and the child turned a blotched, swollen face to Annie. Her dark hair was in a long plait. She was very thin, with a heart-shaped, elfin face and very large eyes. Something in the tear-drenched dark brown gaze made Annie's heart contract. And a belated thought occurred to her: was she English, or Greek?

'*Milaeis angleeka*?' she tried hopefully, calling on her small reserve of Greek. 'Do you speak English?'

The tears abated. The child plugged a thoughtful thumb into a rosebud mouth and sucked in silence, staring at Annie with the kind of analytical curiosity only small children could achieve.

'Your teddy bear is getting wet,' Annie pointed out reasonably. 'I'm not sure that teddy bears can swim. Do you think they can?'

'No.'

That answered that question, at least, Annie thought. Even though the response had been muffled around a thumb, the child wasn't Greek. Presumably an English family had taken the villa next to hers, and had forgotten to keep an eye on their small offspring. Annie rapidly revised her vision of an uninterrupted week of total peace and relaxation. The two villas were set sufficiently apart for privacy, but they shared the hill path and the beach, and their terraces adjoined at one end, through a screen of bamboo and oleander.

She didn't mind too much, she decided. Being the eldest of three, and in the past often put in charge of her younger siblings, she'd discovered that she rather liked small children. Her week could be about to liven up considerably, by the look of things...

'Will you tell me your name?'

'Zoey.'

'Annie Trevellick.' She held out her hand solemnly and, after a short pause, Zoey held out her own small hand and they shook in formal greeting. 'How do you do, Zoey? And what's your bear's name?'

'Emile.'

Annie eyed the smart red dress. 'Emile? Not Emily?'

'He's called Emile. He's a boy.'

'Right. Shall I hold him for you, while we look for your mummy and daddy?'

Zoey put her thumb back in her mouth and shook her head. But, with touching innocence, she held up her hand for Annie to take, and allowed herself to be helped to her feet and led back onto the beach.

With her head bent to talk to Zoey, the thud of running feet on the sand was the first signal that someone else had joined them on the beach.

When Annie looked up and saw the tall man approaching them with athletic speed, her jaw dropped in shocked disbelief. The rush of acute pleasure she felt took her by complete surprise. She realised she was ridiculously happy to see him, glowing inside. She was appalled at her emotional response, considering the way they'd parted…

'Josh!' It was Zoey who shrieked his name, tugging free of Annie's hand and running towards him, even dropping the beloved Emile in her desperate rush to meet him. Annie stood there, stunned, as the child was scooped up into Josh's arms, where she wrapped thin arms round his neck, hid her face against his white polo shirt and promptly burst into loud sobs again.

Over the child's head, as he murmured teasingly and reassuringly to her, Josh met Annie's eyes with a blank enquiry which convinced her that he was as surprised to see her as she was to see him. She was grateful that the distraction of Zoey's greeting had given her time to compose herself.

He looked haggard, she registered, staring at him, even though he was deeply tanned and wore casual, holiday clothes. Beige cotton Bermudas and tan leather deck-shoes revealed long, athletic brown legs; the loose white polo shirt and white baseball cap gave him an air of laid-back relaxation. But there was definitely a tinge of strain in his face…

'This is a happy coincidence, Annie,' he managed, having soothed Zoey's sobs to an acceptable level. 'Dare I hope that my luck is in and that you'll also have a change of heart?'

'A change of heart…?' She gazed at him equally blankly. Meeting him like this, on the beach, seemed to have thrown her into bewildered confusion.

'You'll decide that we do have something to talk about?' he persisted, wryly helpful. 'Its okay, Zoey. This is Annie…a friend of mine.'

Annie bent to pick up the small teddy bear and handed it to Zoey.

'You dropped Emile.' She gave the child a warm smile before eyeing Josh with a touch more caution. 'I'm not sure that we do have much to say to each other,' she prevaricated with a calm she was far from feeling, 'but this is certainly a coincidence. In fact, if it hadn't been for the machinations of my mother and my sister I wouldn't be here at all. They bought me my air ticket and packed me off here for a ''well-earned break'', as they put it… Oh, wait a minute…' She stopped, a sudden possibility occurring to her. 'Did they know you'd be here?'

His smile was mirthless. 'No way. I didn't know myself until last night.'

She looked quickly from the child's tear-stained face to Josh's grim expression. 'What's going on, Josh? Who is she?'

'My god-daughter.' He expelled his breath on a short, rueful laugh. 'It's a long story, Annie. I'll explain some time, if you're interested.'

'Thanks,' she said coolly, crossing her arms over her chest and burrowing one foot into the soft sand beneath her. She felt a twinge of guilt. This, presumably, was the mysterious 'something' that had happened to detain him abroad—a genuine excuse, not a vague fabrication to extract himself from an awkward romantic liaison. Maybe she'd misjudged him…

Anger at herself made her speak more sharply than she intended.

'It's nothing to do with me, Josh. But if you're supposed to be in charge of her she seems very young to be left to run down the hill path by herself. When I found her she was very upset about something…'

His face tightened.

'Criticism acknowledged,' he drawled, equally cool. 'I'm not exactly experienced at caring for three-year-olds, but I thought she was with Eleni.'

'Eleni?' The reaction inside her was like an unexpected white-hot needle, and she tensed in self-disgust. What was the matter with her? Hoping her face didn't reveal the turmoil beneath, she arched her eyebrows in mocking enquiry. 'Zoey's mother, I presume?'

'Wrong. Eleni's a local girl who has been helping to look after Zoey. Zoey's mother died a couple of years ago.' Josh spoke with gentle reproach, the look in his eyes making her squirm with awareness. He had seen that painful flash of reaction. Pride made her tighten her arms across her chest, furious with herself.

'Zoey's father died last week; he was the colleague I told you about, the one that went missing. You probably heard it on the news.'

'Oh, no…oh, Josh.' Annie swallowed a lump in her throat, her antagonism fading beneath a rush of sympathy for the child. 'That's terrible. Is there anything I can do to help?'

He made a wry face.

'To help who? Me? Or Zoey?' he enquired sardonically.

'Zoey,' she said shortly, her eyes softening on the small, wary face of the child clinging to Josh's neck and watching this adult exchange. 'All I meant,' she went on stiffly, blushing slightly, 'was that I like children; and…and in the circumstances, obviously, I'd be happy to help out if necessary. Anyone would feel the same…'

Her mind went quickly over the contents of Villa Kalimaki. 'I don't know about your sister's villa, but there are games and toys in ours; in fact I'm sure there's still a complete set of Mr Men and Noddy books in Meggie's bedroom, and probably some old drawing-books and crayons, although she wouldn't thank me for telling you. I'm quite experienced at keeping small children entertained…'

'Thanks, Annie.' She was almost sure that Josh's dark

blue eyes held no sarcasm; certainly, genuine gratitude seemed to be in his voice. 'I appreciate that. Are you free to drop in for a drink this evening? Maybe we could talk about it?'

'Of course.' She inclined her head awkwardly, turning to walk away.

'Want Annie to carry me,' a small voice announced imperiously. Annie stopped, exchanging a surprised glance with Josh. 'Want Annie...'

'You're too heavy, honeybun.' Josh swung the little girl in the air, and hefted her up and down. 'Annie couldn't carry you all the way up the hill.'

Annie watched the rosebud mouth pucker again, and laughed.

'Let's try, shall we?' She held out her arms, and Zoey came to cling to her neck instead of Josh's. The little girl smelled of baby shampoo, and was as light as a feather. 'I think I can manage to carry you part of the way,' she conceded solemnly, 'even though there are three hundred steps.'

The dark eyes were round.

'Three hundred steps? How do you know there are three hundred steps?'

The climb to the top was taken up with Annie's explanations and Zoey's frequent questions, and by the time they'd reached the point where the path branched in two, leading off to each villa, Annie was more out of breath than she'd expected. Josh, who'd followed in amused silence, gently extricated Zoey and eyed Annie up and down with a degree of concern.

'Sorry; she's heavier than you think. Did you say you were supposed to be out here for a rest?'

'More mental than physical.' She mocked herself quietly. 'Family and friends have swooped in and practically dismissed me from my own business. They seemed convinced I was cracking up.'

Josh frowned, his probing gaze sending shivers of reaction through her.

'How come? Are you okay, Annie?'

'I'm fine, as you can see.' She shrugged. 'Maybe I was cut out to be a lady of leisure.'

'I thought you seemed to be burning the proverbial candle at both ends,' he commented slowly, searching her face with an intimate gleam in his eyes which made her blush again. 'I'm sorry if I made things worse that night…'

Annie stiffened. She glanced meaningfully at Zoey, keeping her voice level with an effort.

'You didn't,' she said lightly, fighting with the scarlet tide threatening to set her whole body, as well as her face, on fire. Josh seemed so kind, so…caring at times, she could almost forget her grievances and risk showing him how much she was growing to like him. She had to fight quite hard with the dangerous urge to put her arms round him, right now, and hug him…

'I'm feeling great already, after a day's swimming and sunbathing and lounging with a novel,' she finished up quickly.

'Good. I'm glad you weren't traumatised by the experience,' he murmured, watching the colour surge and recede in her face, his mouth twisting as Zoey began to struggle to get down. His gaze was dragged reluctantly from Annie's as the child ran off towards the villa with surprising speed. 'I'd better go and check she gets there safely. Mislaying small children in one's charge is always embarrassing.'

'Small children need constant supervision. They're hard work, especially if you're not used to them…' Annie stopped, drawing a steadying breath. 'Sorry; I'm sounding like a prim know-it-all, aren't I? How long have you got her for?'

'That depends on how things work out.' His tone was

unfathomable. 'Don't worry, the situation is under reasonable control. I won't hold you to your offer of help.'

'I wouldn't have made it if I hadn't meant it.'

His blue gaze was hard to resist as he gave her a fleeting smile.

'Are we calling a truce, then? Come for a meal, Annie. About seven? But don't feel you've got to start playing surrogate nanny. That's supposed to be Eleni's job, when she isn't too busy talking on the phone to her boyfriend in Athens.'

Once back in the peace and quiet of her own villa, Annie went slowly into the cool of her bedroom and absently undressed for a shower, dropping her clothes on the floor as she walked. Her mind was racing.

Finding that Josh was here, in the next-door villa, was disturbing in itself. But Zoey's plight made the whole situation more upsetting, and made her reaction more confusing. Almost as much as her nerves quivered at Josh's presence, her heart ached for the little girl. But she couldn't forget the way her stomach had lurched, the way she'd gone hot and cold, when she'd seen Josh on the beach.

In a wave of despairing frustration, she showered and shampooed her hair, leaving it to dry in the hot evening air while she smoothed on after-sun lotion and decided what to wear. She settled for a long sage-green and white flowered cotton sarong-skirt and a loose, cropped white T-shirt which left her midriff bare. She slipped on some simple jewellery to boost her confidence—gold hooped earrings and a pendant necklace—and brushed her hair behind her ears to hang, loose and casual, down her back.

She decided against make-up. After a day in the sun, all she needed was something to stop her nose from shining and a slick of caramel-coloured lipstick. And the last thing she wanted to do was give Josh the impression that she was making an effort to attract him…

Pushing her feet into tan leather mules, she scanned her reflection in the mirror and then went to fetch her bag. She checked in Meggie's room and put a storybook into the bag, then went back down to the sitting-room, all ready to go. She checked her watch; it was only half-past six.

So eager, she mocked herself scathingly, going out on the terrace and sinking down on the sun-chair to wait. Was this the person who'd strong-mindedly hung up on Josh Isaac only a week ago?

Well, it wasn't Josh she was impatient to see tonight, she assured herself, picking up her paperback thriller again and trying to concentrate on the plot without success. Her feelings had nothing to do with Josh. Zoey was the reason she was anxious to go round. The child's dark eyes haunted her. She couldn't shake off that protective feeling she'd experienced, carrying the small child up the hill. To have lost both parents by the age of three… Annie had no firsthand experience of motherhood, but her imagination was vivid enough to dread such a fate befalling any child of hers…

After twenty minutes she gave in on the novel. There was a connecting gate between the two terraces, but Annie opted for formality. She went out of the front door of the Villa Kalimaki, and followed the driveway around to the front door of the Villa Gallos. Rapping with some trepidation with the heavy brass knocker brought a grey-haired Greek woman to the door, and she was ushered inside with a courteous smile.

'Kyria Trevellick? Kyrios Isaac is upstairs with Zoey. You can go up if you wish.'

Annie went slowly up the carved wooden staircase, following the low sound of Josh's deep voice which came from one of the bedrooms. In the doorway she paused, arrested by the sight.

Zoey, thumb firmly in mouth, was in bed, looking heavy-eyed and sleepy, in a pink and yellow nightdress. Emile, identically clad, was tucked in beside her. Josh, in Levis and short-sleeved denim shirt, was sitting at the foot of the bed, leaning against the wall, long legs sprawled in front of him, intently reading a passage from *Teddy Robinson*, complete with an authentically gruff teddy-bear voice. He glanced up and grinned as Annie came slowly into the room, but didn't stop. She sank quietly into the chair by the bed, and was rewarded by a big smile from Zoey.

'More,' she muttered when Josh came to the end of the story.

'Tomorrow,' he assured her solemnly. 'Go to sleep now, Zoey.'

'Annie kiss me goodnight,' Zoey managed, round her thumb.

'I'd be honoured.' Annie smiled, bending to plant a kiss on one warm pink cheek. 'Night, night, sleep tight…'

'Hope the bugs don't bite,' Zoey finished in a faint, sleepy voice, pulling Emile under the covers with her. 'Night, Annie.'

There was a lump in Annie's throat as she followed Josh downstairs.

'She's adorable, Josh.' Annie accepted a glass of chilled white wine on the terrace, and met Josh's eyes with a rueful smile. 'Poor little scrap. What's going to happen to her?'

'She's in my care for the moment,' Josh said obliquely. He poured himself a large glass of red wine and sat down heavily beside her, on a woven rattan armchair. 'Max wanted her to be.'

'Max was her father? The colleague who was killed?'

she ventured carefully. There was a bleakness about Josh, now that Zoey was tucked up in bed.

'Max Stafford.' He nodded briefly. 'He knew the risks of his job and he was worried about being Zoey's sole parent. The trouble was he adored Zoey, but he was addicted to war reporting. The two passions didn't fit too well together.'

Annie stared over the wooden railings at the glorious Greek island evening, the peachy-mauve sunset beyond the sea, the island of Evvia a long purple hump in the distance.

'So you've brought her here to your sister's villa and enlisted the help of a village girl?' she mused, trying to understand what seemed like rather eccentric behaviour on Josh's part. 'What happens now?'

'Nothing, for the moment. But you've got it wrong. First of all, this is my villa now. I bought it from Charlotte and Petros about six months ago. They've built themselves a bigger place nearer to their hotel.'

'Oh.' Annie assimilated this information. Charlotte was Josh's older sister. She'd married Petros, a Greek hotelier, and they ran their hotel business together on the island.

'Secondly, I didn't bring Zoey out here—she was here already. Max rented the villa from me, and brought her out here for a holiday. Another nanny had just left. I suspect he felt he should give Zoey some "quality time".' Josh's mouth twisted ironically. 'Then he got the call to cover the latest developments in Bosnia and left Zoey with Sophia and Eleni…'

'They're related to your sister's husband?' Annie hazarded, trying to complete the puzzle.

'No. Sophia is an old friend of Petros's mother,' Josh said. 'Eleni is her young niece. Charlotte will help out when she can, but she's flat out working; it's nearly the high season. She's still such a perfectionist, she insists on going to the market herself, at the crack of dawn, to choose fresh produce for the hotel restaurant...'

'At least you've got some of your own family as support. What about Zoey's? Where was she living before her father died? Who normally looked after her while Max was working?

'Max had a flat in Paris. There was a nanny, like I said. She went back to Australia.'

'That poor little child. She hasn't had much stability or security, has she? What about relatives?'

Josh's glance was unfathomable.

'None of any use on Max's side. A couple on the mother's. In England.'

'So...Zoey will go and live with them?'

'Not if there's any justice left in this world.' Josh sounded bleakly angry. 'Max didn't have a high opinion of this set of in-laws.'

'A lot of people don't see eye to eye with their in-laws,' Annie began reasonably. 'That doesn't mean...'

'It's an older half-brother and his wife,' Josh said with a shrug, 'who belong to a strict religious sect and have some very weird, repressive ideas on bringing up their own two children. Max's wife stayed well clear of them, but since she died they've been interfering, criticising Max's arrangements for Zoey...' There was a brief, taut silence, then Josh added hoarsely, 'I saw Max in hospital before he died. He begged me to make sure Zoey didn't go to live with them...'

'Can you do that, as her godfather?'

'He appointed me her legal guardian.'

'That's going to mean a lot of difficulties for you, isn't it? I mean, it's not as if you've got a nine-to-five desk job either, is it?'

Josh let out a long breath and leaned back in his chair, glancing across at her with a haggard smile.

'I appreciate your input, Annie, but I've got a lot of

thinking to do on that score. Do you mind if we talk about something else for tonight?'

She swallowed jerkily, and nodded.

'Of course. Sorry; I didn't mean to sound interfering. It's really none of my business...'

A telephone rang inside the villa. Josh stood up and went in to answer it. She heard him say, 'Veronica. Hello...' His voice dropped.

Annie sat very still, her stomach in knots, trying to deal with the wild mixture of emotions triggered by Josh's one-sided, low-voiced conversation, obviously with Veronica Whitton. She felt taut as a wire. She tried to dismiss thoughts of the beautiful redhead. Save your pain for a worthy cause, she flayed herself. Out there, beyond the peaceful blue horizon, there was another world of war and sudden death—a world that had orphaned Zoey. How could she sit here wallowing in misery over Josh's possible relationship with his ex-girlfriend?

She stood up abruptly and went to stand at the edge of the terrace. She gazed out to sea, watching the white wake of a Flying Dolphin hydrofoil scything its way across the sea. Cicadas scratched and shrilled in the olive groves on the hillside. War and tragedy seemed a million miles away, impossible to contemplate.

There was tension in her shoulders. She eased them back, then realised that Josh had finished on the phone and had come back. He was sitting silently in his chair behind her. She turned, with an attempt at a nonchalant smile. She wouldn't mention the telephone call if he didn't.

'You were saying that the subject of Zoey's future was closed for tonight,' she said at last as the silence lengthened. 'So...what shall we talk about?'

'How about starting with the fiasco of a couple of weeks ago?' Josh suggested quietly.

'No...I'd rather not,' she said quickly. 'As far as I'm concerned, it's forgotten, Josh...'

'Not by me,' he said firmly. He stood up and came to lean on the railing a few feet away from her. He searched her face with a rueful gleam in his eyes. 'If you think I'm going to throw away a coincidence like this, you're crazy.'

'What do you mean?'

'Our meeting here,' he explained patiently. 'A coincidence. A happy one.'

'In your opinion.'

The glint in his eyes had become ominously darker.

'If you think I'd pass up the chance to set things straight,' he stated softly, 'you underestimate me.'

'All right.' She faced him, her heart thudding. 'Tell me, how do you propose to set things straight, Josh?'

'By apologising?' he said softly, his gaze level and unflinching. 'I messed things up that night. I behaved like a sex-crazed idiot. My only excuse is the effect you have on me. I got carried away, as the saying goes...'

'Josh...'

'Just listen. I'm in a confessional mood, but I'll try to be brief.' His quick glance was wryly self-mocking. 'I swear to you that I didn't plan the whole thing. I didn't think you were an easy lay, if that's what you were thinking, and the only thing going through my mind at the time was how much I wanted to make love to you...'

'Purer than the driven snow, in fact?' she said huskily.

'No...I admit that when I went away and thought about it I guess I probably didn't believe your denials about Phoenix...'

She felt herself going hot and cold again.

'Josh, I really don't want to talk about this any more.'

'And if that makes me a cynical, suspicious person I'm guilty of that too. It's just the way I am. I guess I'm not a great optimist when it comes to human nature. I

expect the worst until proved wrong.' He smiled mirthlessly, watching the conflicting emotions crossing her
face. 'I'm grovelling, can't you appreciate that?'

Tears pricked the backs of her eyes, made her throat
tighten. Josh was being sincere, he was opening his
heart, to a degree…but the dark landscape it revealed
made her own heart twist painfully in her chest. The urge
to move closer, put her arms round him, felt overpow-
ering. Pride held her back. Josh's fundamental problem
was that he didn't trust women. No doubt a direct legacy
of his mother's behaviour. It was surely deluding herself
to think she could rescue him from a lifetime of bleak
cynicism, especially since she was a little short on trust
herself where men and affairs of the heart were concerned.

'I didn't ask you to grovel,' she said, swallowing the
hard lump in her throat.

'I know. You're much too sweet to ask a man to
grovel.'

She snatched a shaky breath and forced a smile.

'I'm not sweet at all,' she managed thickly. 'In fact,
when it comes to relationships with the opposite sex,
maybe I'm a bit like you…'

'Then think what we have in common,' he teased
bleakly.

'So as far as that night's concerned,' she went on,
ignoring him, 'forget it, Josh. I…I was partly to blame.
And you…just acted like a typical male. Consider it forgiven and forgotten.'

The dark gleam in his eyes had intensified.

'A "typical male"?' he queried drily. 'Well, since
you've got such a low opinion of me and my fellow sex,
Annie, I might as well carry on behaving the way you
expect me to…'

To her intense dismay, he cupped her hot face in his
hands and dropped a swift, searching kiss on her mouth.

The feel of his mouth on hers was electrifying. She couldn't move or breathe. She began to tremble inside. He lifted his head slowly and searched her face in taut silence, with that heavy-lidded gaze she found so disturbing. If he could see the effect he had on her, she thought in despair, she'd be lost...

His voice was husky when he said, 'Don't panic again. I won't force myself on you. It'll be at your invitation this time, Annie, but I want you. And I may be deluding myself, but I think you want me too.'

He kissed her again, with a tender hunger that made her head spin. And, to her mounting despair, she closed her eyes and kissed him back, warmly and fiercely, with a lamentable lack of control over her response...

CHAPTER SIX

IT TOOK every ounce of Annie's will-power to freeze in his arms and struggle to free herself. But panic saved her. Panic, and the abrupt knowledge that her feelings for Josh ran far deeper than she'd realised—that she could be falling in love with him, a ridiculous thing to do which would leave her vulnerable and open to unimaginable pain if she didn't protect herself from her own stupidity...

Josh stopped abruptly and drew back. There was a short, charged silence, while Annie registered how fast her breathing had become, how her intense response to his kiss seemed to have burned a hot flush over the surface of her skin.

Josh's face was sombre, his blue eyes very bright under lowered lids.

'I'd like to work out what's going on in your head, Annie.'

'I don't know what you mean...' She was hardly being honest, she registered bleakly. But then honesty would hardly be the wise option, in the circumstances...

'You don't? To put it bluntly, you blow hot and cold,' he pointed out gently. 'As I discover to my cost every time I give in to the temptation to touch you and kiss you...'

'I didn't ask you to kiss me!' she protested, hugging her arms round her breasts in dismay. 'Maybe you just...just don't appreciate the impact of your technique?'

'I'll take that as a compliment, although I very much

doubt it was meant to be.' With ironic care, he guided her back to her seat, and passed her her glass of wine.

'I'm getting very confused signals from you,' he persisted, his voice wryly husky, 'so can we be honest with each other? If this is some kind of a game you play when men desire you, fair enough. But put me out of my misery, Annie. What do you want?' he probed softly. 'To be lovers, or just friends?'

She fought down the heat that was threatening to burn her up. This was a nightmare, she thought miserably. He saw her as some kind of sophisticated flirt, who led men on and enjoyed seeing them suffer when she withheld her favours.

Pride made it impossible for her to set him straight. She imagined trying to explain the truth, blurting out something along the lines of 'I know you think I'm into casual, opportunist sex with other people's fiancés, but actually I'm a virgin, and I'm afraid that, in spite of your insulting opinion of me, I might be falling in love with you. So, even though I really do want to, I can't possibly go to bed with you, because you obviously don't love me and it would be a complete disaster...' She winced in silent embarrassment. It was too humiliating to even contemplate...

'Just friends,' she heard herself saying, in a voice quite unlike her own. She longed to be able to say 'Both'. She wished with all her heart in that moment that the situation between them could be simple, that underneath Josh didn't still have this jaundiced view of her, that she could trust him enough to feel she could explain the situation...

'I don't believe you.'

She managed a stiff shrug.

'Then why ask, if you weren't prepared to believe my answer?'

'I guess I prefer not to believe it. But that's my problem, not yours. I find you the sexiest female since Eve. You're under no obligation to reciprocate those feelings. *Steen yia sas*, as the Greeks say,' he murmured, huskily mocking, lifting his glass to her. 'Good health, Annie. Since fate has thrown us together again for the time being, here's to a strictly platonic relationship.'

'That shouldn't be too difficult.' She managed to regain some of her poise, shooting him a wary glance from under her lashes. 'All you have to do is stop jumping on me all the time!'

'No problem,' he assured her, deadpan. 'There'll be no more "jumping" whatsoever. Waste of time. We've proved how physically incompatible we are, haven't we?'

She clenched her teeth, staring out to sea.

'This whole thing is just a joke to you, isn't it?'

'Not at all,' he countered wryly. When she turned back to look at him, his eyes locked with hers. 'I take sexual relationships very seriously indeed. I'm not irresponsible. I wasn't about to get you pregnant the other night, Annie,' he added softly, 'if that's what was on your mind...'

'It wasn't that!' She was hot all over, wishing suddenly that the ground would conveniently open and she could slide mercifully into oblivion.

He regarded her steadily over the rim of his glass, his eyes very blue as he searched her face. She was trapped in that blue gaze, her pulses jumping crazily.

She swallowed convulsively. 'Can we please change the subject?'

Josh stood up abruptly, and in silence went to fetch the wine. He topped up their glasses then sat down again, and took a thoughtful sip from his glass.

'How was the date?'

'Sorry...?'

'The one you mentioned on the telephone, before you told me to get lost.' His bland tone was ominous.

'I don't really think that's any of your business, Josh.'

'Maybe not. But I'm just curious. Is he a long-standing boyfriend? Was I muscling in on someone else's territory? Did you get a last-minute attack of fidelity? Is that what happened that night in your flat, Annie?'

She levelled a look of such disdain at him that Josh had the grace to look slightly abashed. Yet more proof, if she needed any, of how little he trusted women in general. 'A last-minute attack of fidelity'? How derogatory could he get? Even if his low opinion of the female sex did stem from his mother walking out on his father when Josh was ten, the dangerous wave of compassion had to be emphatically suppressed.

'You were right about your suspicious, distrustful mind,' she said quietly. 'I suppose your other involvements don't count?'

'What other involvements?'

'Please don't bother to pretend there's nothing between you and Veronica Whitton. She was drooling all over you at the restaurant in London. She just rang you tonight. You must think I'm a complete idiot, Josh...'

'Not quite,' he commented drily, 'but I'm gratified to see that you're jealous.'

'I am not jealous!'

'Lucky you,' he murmured. 'Jealousy eats you up. Take my advice: never get jealous.' He stood up slowly, a wry gleam of warmth in his eyes sending her into fresh confusion. 'Come on, Annie. Let's go and see what Sophia has cooked for us, shall we?'

Dinner was simple but delicious. Sophia had laid a table at the other end of the large terrace, and happily presented them with aromatic souvlaki—pork and vegetables on a skewer—with rice and potatoes. Tiny tender green beans called fasolakia were served as an accompaniment.

Josh steered the conversation onto uncontroversial topics and, anxious to avoid further tension, Annie quickly picked up the cue. Family and friends were safe ground to stay on. She discovered the source of Josh's bedside-story skills: he was already an uncle twice over. Charlotte and Petros had a boy who was now nearly two, and Camilla had married an extremely acceptable Ivy League graduate back in America and rapidly produced a baby girl, now just over a year old.

In spite of her inner turmoil, she relaxed a bit as they talked. They drank some more of the dry white wine with the meal, and as darkness finally fell they ate by the light of the anti-mosquito candles dotted around the terrace.

'This is such a little paradise.' Annie finished the melon she'd had for dessert, and propped her chin on her hand to gaze at the view. 'It's hard to believe that just a few hundred miles north of here there's a war going on.'

'Wars and violence are a fact of life all over the world.' Josh leaned across to refill her wine glass, draining the bottle between their glasses. 'Life goes on, Annie.'

'It must seem more shocking to you,' she persisted, frowning into her glass, 'coming and going so often between the two extremes? From atrocities and war crimes to the bland indifference of countries not affected?'

Josh was silent. She glanced at him and saw that his jaw was clenched, a pulse flicking in his cheek.

'Sorry,' she said quietly. 'Am I being insensitive? Don't you want to talk about it?'

He turned his brooding gaze on her.

'No. It's okay, Annie. Reporting wars is a kind of

crusade. You feel that someone has to go out there and let the world know what's really happening. But you're quite right—it's a strain. After a few years, the strain can get unbearable. I'm thinking of giving it up, as a matter of fact.'

'Because of Zoey? Or because of what happened to Max?'

His gaze narrowed.

'I presume you mean do I need to make time for Zoey, or have I lost my nerve, seeing a colleague killed?'

She flushed slightly.

'That wasn't exactly what I meant. I'm…I'm just curious, that's all. About your motives…'

'I won't pretend Zoey and Max's tragedy has had no impact on my thinking,' he said flatly. 'But I've been writing a book over the past few months. Recently I've had it accepted, with a request for more of the same, so I've been planning to devote more time to that. Zoey just means I'll do it sooner rather than later.'

'What kind of book?'

'Rather predictably, a political war thriller.' He grinned faintly, seeing her wide-eyed interest. 'They say write about what you know.'

'That's brilliant, Josh—congratulations,' she told him sincerely. 'So, you're going to be famous?'

'Who can say? Don't hold your breath. Shall we have some coffee?'

A piercing scream from upstairs made them both freeze. Josh stood up so abruptly that his chair very nearly toppled over, and with long strides he vanished into the villa. The scream had turned to frantic, heart-rending sobbing. Annie sat indecisively for a few seconds, her hands clenched in her lap at the sound of the pitiful crying, then she could stand it no longer. She went after Josh.

She found him sitting on Zoey's bed, cradling the little girl in his arms, gently stroking her hair. A low night-light burned on the bedside table. Josh looked harassed.

'Can I help?' she ventured softly.

'She had a nightmare, I think.'

'Has this happened before?'

'A couple of times. Shh, honeybun, it's okay. Shh…'

At the sound of Annie's voice, Zoey twisted round and held out her arms. Annie went quickly forward and lifted the child up, cuddling her close to her chest. Holding the small, warm body in her arms, she felt such a rush of emotion, she could hardly breathe for a few seconds.

'Want my daddy,' Zoey was sobbing. 'Where's my daddy?'

Over Zoey's head, Annie silently sought Josh's eyes. He rubbed a hand over his forehead, grimacing slightly. She sat down close to Josh, so that Zoey was between them.

'Sweetheart,' she said quietly, 'Your daddy…your daddy loves you very much and he always will, but he's had to go away—'

'Remember, Zoey?' Josh cut in quietly. 'Your daddy went to heaven, honeybun…'

'Where Mummy went?' The sobs were abating. Zoey's voice was muffled round her thumb, her small face flushed as she eyed them both with wary, tear-bright eyes.

'The same place your mummy went.'

'Is it nice?'

'It's a really nice place.' Josh cleared his throat, closing his eyes, a pulse twitching at the corner of his compressed mouth. He looked so shattered and exhausted suddenly. Annie felt her whole body vibrate with sympathy for them both.

'Your daddy was very special and God needed your daddy in heaven with Him,' Annie finished for him, her voice husky. She blinked, and dropped a kiss on the hot, damp forehead against her chest.

'Can't I go too?'

'No, not for a long time. God...God wants you to stay here...with us,' Annie assured her firmly, abruptly conscious of the raw intimacy of this situation. As she caught Josh's eye over Zoey's head, her heart lurched uncontrollably. 'Stay here with us'? What in the world was she saying?

'That's right, poppet,' Josh murmured, his tone less ragged. 'Go back to sleep now.'

Zoey climbed back into bed with an exhausted droop to her small shoulders, and clutched her teddy bear as her eyelids closed.

'I like Annie,' she announced sleepily. 'Can I stay here with you and Annie, Josh?'

Josh's gaze met Annie's, his expression bleakly amused.

'We'll both be around in the morning.'

'Promise?' she demanded, thumb in mouth.

'Promise. Night, Zoey.' Josh ushered Annie out of the room and pulled the door to, avoiding her eyes until they were down on the terrace again. The haunted bleakness she saw in his face made her heart contract.

'Josh, you're doing a great job,' she said softly. 'I really admire you. A lesser man would have run a mile from this, believe me...'

'I'm doing nothing particularly admirable,' he said flatly. 'What else could I do? She's defenceless; she needs protection, from life in general and from her relatives in particular.'

'I still think you're doing a wonderful job. You'd...you'd make a great father,' she assured him, suddenly awkward as she read the hint of bleak amusement returning to his eyes.

'Would I indeed?' he said, grinning. The humour lingered briefly, then faded. 'You know what haunts me most, Annie? It's that Max died doing my job.'

'What?' She stared up at him in bewilderment.

'I was tied up in Cornwall at the wedding. So they contacted Max in my place. Lord knows, I can't seem to shake off the feeling of guilt.'

Annie bit her lip, her throat tightening.

'Josh, that's rubbish; you know it is,' she told him with quiet conviction. 'Max didn't die in anyone's place. He was just unlucky. You said yourself he was totally addicted to the job. He died doing what he felt to be his vocation...'

She saw the shadowed tension in his expression and, without thinking, blindly reached out to wrap her arms round his broad shoulders. He tensed for a second and then pulled her against him, and then, without warning, they were crushed in an embrace which felt shudderingly familiar.

When he searched for her mouth with his, brushed his lips questioningly over hers, she parted her lips involuntarily. Then he was kissing her with that addictive, banked-down passion which sent shafts of bitter-sweet pleasure right to the ends of her fingers and toes.

He drew back abruptly, his breathing ragged, his expression unreadable. She felt hot all over. She wanted him so badly that if he'd picked her up and carried her to his bed right then she'd have melted in his arms, all her good intentions dissolved...

'Sorry.' He sounded huskily mocking. 'I forgot. We're strictly platonic now, aren't we?'

She opened her mouth to speak, but with a short laugh he turned away to gaze out to sea. She was rooted to the spot, feeling confused and ridiculously tongue-tied. She was ashamed to feel the physical evidence of Josh's effect on her—the way her nipples tingled tightly beneath her crop-top, the heavy warmth in her stomach and thighs. Folding her arms across her chest, she fought to steady her breathing.

'You seem to have been temporarily co-opted as chief mother substitute for Zoey,' Josh said at last, turning back to look at her. 'It's quite an imposition. Do you mind, Annie?'

'Of course I don't mind,' Annie assured him quietly, sitting down carefully and picking up the glass with the remains of her wine, her hand shaking slightly. 'It seems to me that...that Zoey needs a lot of reassurance from the adults around her. She's frightened and confused, and...' she shrugged slightly '...well, if there's something in me that fills a void in her life I'm more than willing to be there for her, for the moment... I'm sure there'll be some way I can keep in touch with her when I'm back in London...' She was floundering inwardly.

Josh was silent for a while, leaning on the wooden railing. His strong, hard-featured face was half in shadow, half in candlelight. It made him look distant, enigmatic, like a complete stranger.

'That's a very mature way of thinking. You surprise me all the time, Annie. Not precisely what the doctor ordered for your rest period, though, is it?'

She shrugged again.

'A change is as good as a rest. Isn't that what they say?'

'Nor is it precisely what the doctor ordered for Zoey,' Josh added expressionlessly.

'Well...'

'Zoey needs continuity.'

'In an ideal world, yes, but...'

'Don't tell me about ideal worlds, Annie,' he said, smiling bleakly. 'In an ideal world, Zoey wouldn't be an orphan at the tender age of nearly four. Or, failing that, you and I would be an ''item'', as they say, and little Zoey would therefore have stumbled across a pair of people equipped to offer her all the security and continuity she needs. But in the flawed world she's been thrown into, unfortunately, the opposite applies.'

Annie stiffened, draining her wine glass. Josh's ruthless analysis of the situation hit her like a physical blow. She felt out of her depth, and unaccountably bereft.

'Are you telling me to…to back off?' she asked simply.

He shrugged, his eyes expressionless.

'God only knows, Annie, a mother is the most precious gift a child can possess. Anyone who can step into that role and give it genuine commitment has my vote, for sure…'

She stared at him, her heart jolting.

'You sound as if you speak from experience,' she risked saying lightly. 'Did…did you have a mother substitute as a child, Josh? After your mother left?'

He slanted her a dark look.

'I had a whole series of them, Annie,' he confirmed. 'But they didn't have much staying power. Their affair with my father would come to an end, and they moved on. I sometimes got too attached to them. When I got older, I decided the ones who didn't pretend to be mother substitutes were the kindest, in the long run.'

Her heart felt tight with sympathy. Had she just been honoured by a rare glimpse beneath the cool exterior of Josh Isaac, tough foreign correspondent? Josh really didn't trust women, she reflected, confirming her earlier thoughts. And no wonder. But, even while she understood, even while her heart ached for him, on another level she was deeply hurt. Why should he imply that she was just like those long-ago women in his life, just like his real mother, even…?

'Are you saying I should keep my distance from that little girl?'

'No. Hell, no! Quite the opposite. In fact—' He

stopped abruptly. She stared at him in blank bewilderment.

'Go on...' she said at last, when Josh's brooding pause seemed destined to go on indefinitely.

He expelled a long breath, and shot her a wry smile.

'I have a plan to run by you. I'd value your opinion on it, Annie. But...I guess I need a little longer to think how to phrase it,' he told her enigmatically. 'Would you like that coffee now?'

'Yes...all right. Thank you,' she agreed warily.

'Right. I'll go and make some.'

She followed him slowly into the kitchen, her mind reeling. A plan? Try as she might, she was quite unable to imagine what kind of plan Josh could be formulating. Pride and caution made her refrain from probing.

'Have Sophia and Eleni gone?'

He nodded over his shoulder. 'They only stayed over-night to look after Zoey when Max went away—since I've been here, they've come up from the village each day.'

She stood in the doorway, hovering uncertainly. The room was spotless, the surfaces gleaming, rosewood cupboards elegantly closed. Pots, pans and dinner plates were nowhere to be seen; a dishwasher chugged quietly to itself in one corner. Sophia was clearly a fast, efficient worker, even by her own exacting standards, Annie noted automatically.

'I'll make the coffee, Josh,' she offered, the memory of his harassed air upstairs in Zoey's bedroom swimming into her mind. 'You go back and relax on the terrace...'

Josh took a Perspex coffee jug down from a shelf and flicked on the kettle. He gave her a wry glance as he unscrewed a jar of coffee grounds and spooned some into the jug.

'You're determined to pull your weight, aren't you?' he teased gently. 'Do you find it impossible to let someone else do things for you? You sit down and relax, Annie. You're supposed to be out here resting, aren't you?'

Chastened, she went to sit on a stool. Liv's remark about delegating had sprung to mind. She supposed it was true; she did have a feeling she had to do everything herself. Her father affectionately called her 'hyperactive'. She silently resolved to try and adjust her style of working when she got back to London...

'I was just trying to be helpful,' she said lightly. 'You make that sound like a crime.'

'It wasn't meant to. You strike me as a very...caring person, Annie,' he said calmly, the mockery fading. 'The more I see of you, the more I like what I see.'

'Really?' She kept her voice wry, willed herself not to melt under that deadly charm. Common sense told her that compliments from Josh Isaac shouldn't affect her quite so dramatically; after all, the warm glow they gave her could hardly cancel out his basic, weary contempt for her and the rest of the female population. 'That's not what you were implying earlier—that I've been leading you on? I blow hot and cold?'

'Okay, okay...' He held up his hand. 'So nobody's perfect. That doesn't mean I can't appreciate your...finer points.'

'You've got weird taste in women, then.'

'Quite possibly.'

He was laughing, and she found herself laughing with him. A warmth had crept into the atmosphere. She felt a strong temptation to relax completely, to dismiss her fears and let her violent attraction to Josh take its natural course.

But she was a coward, she reflected unhappily as they took the tray of coffee out onto the terrace again. She sat down while Josh poured her a cup and added just the right quantity of cream. She must be a coward, she thought, taking the coffee and sipping it gratefully. Otherwise she'd be honest and open, if only to herself, and admit her feelings for him...

'You look pensive,' he commented, when the silence had lengthened.

She glanced at him, glad of the dim candlelight.

'I'm just sleepy,' she lied, taking a cup of coffee. 'I'd better go. What was this mysterious plan you wanted my opinion on?'

His eyes heavy-lidded, he turned to search her face. He said nothing for so long, she felt her nerves beginning to fray.

'Josh?' she prompted finally, with a short laugh. 'Don't just sit there studying me as if...as if I were an object of curiosity or something; tell me what this is about. What's this plan of yours?'

'Okay,' he said at last. He sounded detached, almost businesslike. 'It's not so much a plan as a solution to my problem. Zoey is my first priority right now. I feel a strong obligation to protect her from any further trauma in her life. I told you that I promised Max, just before he died, that I wouldn't allow her to go and live with her relatives...'

He stopped, took a mouthful of black coffee, and was silent again for a few moments.

'Unfortunately, it looks as if I might have a legal battle on my hands,' he went on flatly. 'The half-brother's solicitors have indicated that they're suing for custody of Zoey. And, whilst I'm technically her legal guardian and her godfather, they're apparently challenging the legality of Max's arrangements...'

'Can they do that?'

'Anyone can challenge anything through the courts if they've got enough money.' Josh sounded cynical. 'Zoey's relatives have plenty of that; they live in an impressive town house in London, from what Max told

me. I'm told they're basing their objections on the un-
suitability of a bachelor with a high-powered job caring
for a small girl of Zoey's age. They feel they have some
special calling to provide a secure home for the child.
The trouble is that their notion of a secure home was
Max's notion of a fundamentalist prison.'

She stared at him in concern.

'So what can you do?'

His blue gaze was wryly contained.

'My advisors tell me the best thing I can do is stop
being a bachelor. I need to find myself a suitable wife.
As quickly as possible.'

Annie continued to stare at him in incomprehension,
until, abruptly, the impact of his words sank in.

'Find yourself a wife?' she echoed blankly.

'Correct.'

She felt herself growing hot. In a voice which sounded
completely unlike her own, she said, 'Did you...I mean,
have you got someone in mind?'

'The ideal candidate doesn't instantly spring to mind,'
he admitted coolly, meeting her wide-eyed gaze with a
noncommittal expression. 'Conventionally, people tend
to marry for love after a civilised period of courtship.
And conventionally children tend to follow on in a year
or two. In this case, I'd be expecting some woman not
only to tie the knot in a hurry but also to immediately
take on the role of surrogate mother to Zoey. And I'm
not talking about a temporary arrangement. I want someone who'll be a mother to Zoey, someone who'll give
her all the love and care a little girl needs, someone I
can trust not to let her down. I'm not sure how many
females with such nobly self-sacrificing natures are going to be available for the job.'

'Maybe it would depend on what they felt was in it
for them?' she managed, her voice strained.
'Since...since you're making it sound like a business

deal, you could maybe come to some kind of arrangement that would suit both of you?'

'You're suggesting I consult my address book and give a few of my female acquaintances a ring, run the idea by them?' he said mildly.

'Well...' Her throat felt as if it might close completely, choke her to death. She sipped some more coffee in quiet desperation. 'No, that's not exactly what... I mean, what are you asking me to do? Are you telling me this because...because you think I could find you someone suitable?'

'Suitable is the key word.' He nodded thoughtfully. 'The complication is that I have to find a suitable wife— someone I'd trust to give Zoey all the love and patience she needs. That disqualifies the hard-bitten female journalists of my acquaintance who view children in the same light as the child-catcher in *Chitty Chitty Bang Bang*.'

'You must be acquainted with some woman who isn't like that,' Annie managed dejectedly. All she could think of was keeping her poise, getting through this surreal conversation, then escaping to her own villa to hide her agony. 'Your biggest problem will be working out how to...how to persuade her that this loveless marriage has sufficient advantages to her to make such an enormous commitment worth her while...'

He turned to eye her with a calm, dissecting glint in his eyes.

'True. Well, obviously, it wouldn't be a normal marriage,' he added, with a short laugh. 'The lucky lady and I could hardly fake the love affair of the century, with so little time to whip up enthusiasm for each other. But, I guess as long as we agreed to put Zoey's needs first, we could have one of those pre-nuptial contracts drawn up, if she wanted. One which could be to her financial advantage, if she had any money problems. Shortage of cash isn't one of my problems. We could even have one which stated we were entitled to discreetly seek our sexual satisfaction elsewhere, since I imagine emotional commitment would be out of the question...'

Annie's hand was shaking as she returned her coffee cup to its saucer. The tell-tale rattle made her tense up even more. She could hear the drumming of blood in her ears as she clenched her hands in her lap. She felt so upset and angry, she wasn't sure what was tearing her apart the most.

Did Josh seriously expect someone to agree to this, when he so clearly looked on the whole thing as a cold-blooded business deal?

Avoiding Josh's eyes, she stifled a genuine yawn, partly caused by tiredness and partly by nerves.

'It's an interesting dilemma.' She was dismayed to hear how choked her voice sounded as she stood up, to realise how near to tears she appeared to be. 'But I'm sorry, I can't see how I'm supposed to solve it for you. So, if you'll excuse me, I'm really tired. Thanks for the meal. I'm going to bed. Goodnight.'

'Hey...'

She'd begun to leave through the villa, but he stopped her, grasping her arm and turning her back to face him.

'Where are you rushing off to?'

'I just told you, I'm tired...'

'Have I upset you?' he probed softly, catching her chin between his thumb and finger and lifting her white face to the light. 'Annie?'

'No, not at all...'

'Then why walk all the way round,' he said drily, 'when there's a connecting gate between the terraces? And why dash off without your bag?'

'Oh...' Screaming inwardly, she bent to pick up her bag. She suddenly felt acutely self-conscious, body-conscious. She could feel his eyes on her, on the soft movement of her breasts beneath the cropped T-shirt, before she straightened up. A wave of shivery heat engulfed her as she faced him again. A hot, traitorous tear welled up and rolled slowly down her cheek, and she dashed it away furiously with the back of her hand.

'Annie, what's wrong?' The expression in his eyes held concern, but no other discernible emotion.

'What's wrong?' she burst out softly. 'If you don't know what's wrong, Josh, then I'm quite sure I couldn't explain it to you…!'

'Try.'

'All right. I'm not sure what I find the most upsetting, Josh—the idea of your…your marrying some suitable female purely to win your court case for Zoey or the idea of Zoey being subjected to the whims of some unknown woman who might go along with the plan for ulterior motives…'

'Right.' He hesitated a moment, his heavy-lidded gaze darkening. 'Hell, it looks as if I overestimated your powers of perception, Annie…'

'Really? Well, I am female, after all!' she shot back fiercely, choking back the tears. 'Not surprising I'm short on perception, is it? On your scale of values women probably score nil out of ten in every respect…'

'Annie…' There was a shudder of gentle laughter in Josh's voice which stopped her short. Then he took hold of her shoulders, which made her breath dry up in her chest. 'That's not true. I don't know where you got that idea about me, but I swear it's not true. When I said you were short on perception, I meant you obviously hadn't noticed my rather offbeat proposal of marriage.'

'Your what…?' The shock at least dried her tears.

'I'm sorry, I didn't have the guts to just ask you outright. But I'm asking you now. I'm asking you to marry me, Annie. On…on the stated conditions, naturally…'

If her jaw dropped much further it might fall off completely, she registered. She hurriedly shut her mouth. He dug in his pocket and produced a clean white handkerchief.

'Here.' He handed it to her with a wry half-smile. 'I've taken to carrying these with me at all times lately. Zoey's influence.'

She pressed the cool linen to her eyes, and blew her nose.

'Josh,' she began carefully, her breathing unsteady, 'if this is your idea of a joke…'

'The handkerchief?'

'The proposal of marriage!'

'I'm deadly serious,' he assured her quietly. 'I need to make sure that Zoey has someone I can trust to take care of her. I need a wife to ensure that I can keep custody of Zoey. Zoey needs a surrogate mother.'

'Why me?' She felt as if she was clinging to the cliff of her composure by her fingernails.

'I'd rather have you around for Zoey than any other woman I know.' There was an unreadable gleam in the blue gaze holding hers. 'There's a warmth, a sweetness in your nature, Annie. You've got a lot of natural love to offer a child. They're rare commodities. They're what little Zoey needs. If you can rise above the deficiencies in our relationship, and tackle the challenge for Zoey, I'll be forever in your debt. It may not seem much of a deal, but I'll do my best to make it worth your while. The job's yours if you'll do it, Annie.'

She sat down abruptly on the rattan sofa. She was so stunned, she felt as if all the breath had been extracted from her lungs.

After a while, Josh sat down beside her.

'Is the idea so depressing?' he asked huskily. He reached out and took her hand, holding it between both of his, with what felt like genuine tenderness.

She shook her head wordlessly, glancing at him. Her

heart contracted again. He appeared so tense and wary. 'Sorry,' she said shakily, 'but I don't know what to say...'

'Don't worry,' he reassured her stiffly. 'I'd like to know your answer, Annie, but if you need time to think about it I can quite understand that...'

She bit her lip, taking a long, ragged breath. Closing her eyes, she let her imagination rapidly picture her two choices for the future: the safe, sensible one, the one without Josh and Zoey, in which she endured endless regrets and if-onlys, but kept her pride and her heart and her sanity intact, and the reckless, risky one, the one with Josh and Zoey as her ready-made family—vulnerable little Zoey whose small world had been turned upside down, who depended on whichever adults took the initiative and tried to fill that world with love and security. And Josh. Josh, as her husband...

That prospect made her insides feel as if they were folding in on themselves. Josh, her husband. Mrs Josh Isaac. How did she feel about that? She felt more, much more than a kind of shy desire for him.

In stressed silence, she stared the painful truth in the face. Josh didn't love her. In fact he probably didn't know how to genuinely love and trust a woman. But, if she was being offered the opportunity to try to create a real family for Zoey, with Josh, she knew she couldn't turn it down...

Because she loved him. She loved him desperately. She would never feel this way about any other man. And she desperately wanted to help little Zoey.

'Annie?' His deep voice cut in harshly on her silent agony. She turned, and looked into narrowed, searching eyes that were so dark, the blue had turned to black.

'Yes?'

'Do you want a few days to think it over?'

She sighed unsteadily and forced her mouth into a parody of a smile.

'No. I don't need to think it over. I've already decided...'

'So?' There was a roughness in his voice which made her throat feel tight. 'For God's sake, Annie, will you do it?'

'Yes, Josh,' she told him, in a surprisingly calm voice. 'Yes, I will.'

CHAPTER SEVEN

ORGANISING a wedding at a moment's notice was no simple matter, Annie acknowledged, putting down the telephone for the tenth time that day and feeling grateful for the miracle of long-distance calling.

Was she mad to be doing this? She'd asked herself that question over and over again since she'd heard herself huskily agreeing to Josh's astonishing 'job' offer. Attempts to rationalise her decision to herself were pointless, she'd decided at last, because the decision wasn't rational, it was emotional...

She'd had several difficult conversations on the phone with Liv, who was agog at the news and not prepared to accept the apparent *fait accompli* without a lot of awkward, searching questions.

'Derrick's none too happy about it,' she'd said teasingly. 'He came round yesterday demanding to know where he could contact you!'

'But why on earth should he mind?' Annie had protested. 'Heavens, we only ever went out as friends!'

'Maybe he didn't see it that way.'

'I can't help that, can I?' she'd retorted, more sharply than she'd intended. She wasn't good at explaining her innermost feelings. She'd always tended to keep her personal problems to herself, a legacy of being the eldest of the family, perhaps—the one everyone else came to for advice rather than the other way around. Even so, it was hard this time to be evasive with Liv, especially when she longed to confide in her sister.

But she knew Liv and her romantic ideals. If Liv knew about the pre-nuptial contract currently being drawn up with cold-blooded precision by a solicitor friend of Josh's, detailing all the sensible, logical arrangements she and Josh had discussed for the benefit of Zoey, she'd immediately interrogate her on her real motives. And, if she did that, Annie didn't think she had any chance of fooling Liv. Liv would perceive that, whilst Josh might look on the arrangement as a kind of marriage of convenience, Annie was irrevocably, fathoms-deep in love with Josh. And, once Liv guessed, and once she knew that Josh didn't realise that Annie loved him, she'd feel compelled to interfere, loyal and well-meaning, the way she'd interfered at Miles and Alison's wedding reception. Annie wasn't sure her pride could take such a potentially rich source of humiliation...

'Do you like my picture?' Zoey jumped up from the table in the shade and ran across the terrace with a large sheet of paper she'd been working on intently for the last half an hour. Josh had flown back to London for a couple of days, to make various arrangements, and they'd agreed that she'd move into Villa Gallos to reassure Zoey that he'd be back, and that Annie was here to care for her while he was away. He was due back today, thought Annie. She wondered fleetingly what Josh would say if he knew how desperately she'd missed him, even for such a short time.

'Mmm...I like it very much,' Annie said solemnly as she sat down, widening her eyes at the hectic lines and circles, the dramatic swirls of colour. 'It's a beautiful picture, Zoey...'

'It's you and Josh,' Zoey informed her, looking slightly hurt by Annie's obtuseness. 'See?'

With a slow nod, Annie perceived the likeness.

'How silly of me,' she told the little girl, smiling at the wide, anxious gaze. 'Of course it is. There's Josh's dark hair and my blonde hair. You're good at drawing, Zoey. Do you like it?'

Zoey climbed onto her lap, and agreed that she did.

'Daddy used to paint pictures when he wasn't at work,' the child confided, taking a thick lock of Annie's hair and clutching it in her hand as she thrust her thumb into her mouth.

'I expect you take after him,' Annie said, cuddling Zoey close to her, dropping an absent kiss on the small, dark head. A sound on the terrace made her look up. Josh had appeared round the corner of the villa, and was standing there quietly, watching them. For a few seconds she met his eyes with that now familiar lurch in her heart, until she had her emotions under control.

'Hi,' she called casually, waiting for Zoey to jump down and excitedly run to greet him before getting slowly to her feet, her heart now wisely numb. 'Did you have a successful trip?'

'Moderately,' he smiled, walking towards her with Zoey clutching his hand. 'I've organised everything I can think of. Martha Betts, my dear old housekeeper, is more than happy to be permanent nanny and babysitter, as long as you and Zoey approve, of course. She's standing by with a vast quantity of toys and a box of confetti...'

'She's not a Mrs Danvers, like the housekeeper in *Rebecca*, then?' The forced joke sounded hollow the moment she said it.

'Hardly—more like Mary Poppins. Besides, there's no first Mrs Isaac for her to be insanely loyal to, is there?' Josh lifted a mocking eyebrow.

'You tell me,' she taunted lightly. 'You could have any number of skeletons in your cupboard, Josh.'

'You can always check with Miles,' he suggested calmly. 'He'd probably have noticed if I'd done away with a previous wife. Oh, by the way...' he was delving into the pocket of the light beige linen jacket he was carrying '...ritual decrees that you have one of these.'

He held out a small, dark red velvet box, and Annie

felt her throat dry as she stared at it. Her palms suddenly felt damp. She wiped them down the front of her short, flower-sprigged tan and white sundress, then pushed her hair from her eyes.

'What is it?'

'An engagement ring?' Josh suggested mildly, watching the colour drain from her face with a flicker of concern. 'Are you all right, Annie? Not having second thoughts, are you?'

'Yes…no…' She took the box with trembling fingers and triggered the catch. The box sprang open to reveal a brilliant solitaire diamond, nestling in a bed of red satin. Her throat closed up completely. Speechless, she took it from the box and tried it on the correct finger. It fitted perfectly. The diamond looked large and expertly cut and very expensive, flashing fire at her in the afternoon sun. Surrounding it were tiny seed pearls. She stared at it for a long time.

'It's beautiful. How did…?' She caught her breath, and battled with the ridiculous waves of completely inappropriate and dangerous emotion. 'How did you know what size I needed?'

'I saw Liv,' he explained casually, lifting a hand to greet Sophia as she came out with a tray of drinks. 'She came up with a sample from your jewellery case.'

'Oh. Right…'

'I've also taken the liberty of advising her to take on a couple more cooks to keep your business up and running while we're tied up in the early days with Zoey. Don't worry about the cost,' he added, seeing her beginning to frown in alarm.

'Mr Efficiency,' she said shortly, staring at him in uneasy admiration. Josh appeared to be frighteningly capable of organising everything. So far, she'd had very little to do apart from keep Zoey happy, and alert those closest to her of her imminent change of status. Special licences, registry office bookings, the legalities of Zoey's passport—all had been dealt with by Josh. Over the last few days, she'd felt as if she'd been swept up in a giant whirlwind and hadn't yet been tossed back to earth...

'Come and see my picture.' Zoey was tugging his hand, and he followed her obediently, duly admired the work of art, then sat down with Zoey on his lap while he drank some of the tea Sophia had poured for them. 'I've got a present for you too, honeybunch,' he told her seriously. 'Go and look in the bag.'

Much searching and rustling followed, until Zoey extracted two exquisite little dresses, pink and white striped with small red rosebuds in the white stripes, one in her size and one for Emile. In raptures, she ran off to fetch the teddy bear, and proceeded to exchange his small pair of denim dungarees for the new dress.

'Can me and Emile wear this to your wedding?' she demanded to know, waggling the bear up and down in front of her and proudly admiring the effect.

'Definitely,' Josh assured her, catching Annie's eye and grinning. 'Is she a bit young for grammar lessons, do you think?'

'Slightly.' Annie kept a straight face. 'Where on earth do you find all these little matching outfits, Josh?'

'There's a boutique in London. I discovered it some years ago. I've always done my dutiful godfather bit and bought one for each of Zoey's birthdays. They seemed like the best way of cheering her up, in the present circumstances.'

'Shopping therapy starts young these days. You clearly know the way to young ladies' hearts,' Annie told him, with a smile.

'Do I, Annie?' Josh's answering smile was enigmatic, but she discerned the coolness beneath his words. Her stomach contracted in secret dismay. 'I didn't dare buy anything for you to wear for the ceremony.'

'No…well, I'm sure I'll find something quickly when I get back to London.'

'I didn't mean I wouldn't buy you something,' he amended firmly, draining his teacup and standing up. He looked so attractive in his beige chinos and white, travel-crumpled linen shirt that she blinked and quickly looked away. 'I guess I just didn't know your taste well enough yet to go ahead without you.'

'That's okay.' She felt as if she was walking through a minefield. The protocol of their situation felt so delicately balanced; one false step and the whole shaky edifice would collapse around them. 'I wouldn't expect it…'

'Annie…' Josh stepped closer to her, and to her alarm took her by the shoulders. He held her still in front of him while he studied her carefully controlled expression. His eyes were heavy-lidded but bright with emotion. '*Mea culpa*. I'm not keeping up appearances, am I? I haven't greeted my wife-to-be properly,' he murmured, easing her a fraction closer so that his body heat burned her through the last half inch separating them. 'Very remiss of me…'

She shut her eyes in panic as he lowered his head to seek her mouth with his.

Somehow, since she was supposed to be marrying him solely for Zoey's sake, her traitorous responses to him were even more disturbing. If only she didn't care about him quite so much. But she did, and there was nothing she could do about it. She could do her best to hide her true feelings from Josh, but there was very little point in trying to hide them from herself. Like an idiot, she'd loved him ever since that holiday two years ago, when she'd first seen him windsurfing down there in the bay.

Now, knowing that he might desire her but certainly didn't love her, she'd agreed to this marriage and, in the process, quite possibly condemned herself to a lifetime of emotional torture.

Josh had a warm, humorous side to his nature, but she'd discovered for herself that he also had a jealous, distrustful streak in him, which he seemed to deal with by a kind of world-weary assumption that all women were likely to betray him, at some point. She needed her head examining, she told herself miserably.

She couldn't cite Zoey's plight as her only motive. The most powerful spur of all had been the agonising jealousy she'd felt at the thought of Josh marrying someone else; and she couldn't deny that, in this respect, Veronica Whitton's beautiful face seemed to be indelibly printed on her mind...

She felt a glow of warmth suffuse her whole body as he kissed her with a long, slow, searching expertise which left her knees weak and her stomach a quivering hollow of need. When he released her, she was breathless with the longing to tell him how much she loved him.

'I want a hug too,' Zoey announced crossly, patting at their knees with her small hands, breaking the tension. Abruptly light-headed with relief, Annie looked down and laughed, pushing Josh away with an effort that cost her dearly, and bending to scoop the child up between them.

'You'll always get a hug from Josh and from me,' she told her, kissing the smooth, peachy cheek and ruffling the soft, dark hair. 'We both love you very much.'

'Are you and Josh going to be my mummy and daddy?'

'Yes. Yes, darling, we are.' Annie was annoyed to hear how husky her voice sounded.

Josh had taken a step back. He was smiling, but his eyes looked strained.

'I'm a lucky guy,' he said quietly, any humour that

had been present vanishing like the sun behind a cloud. 'I guess I'd better remember that. How about we all go down to the beach for a swim?'

Zoey's enthusiastic response clinched it. They went to change into swimming gear then made the descent to the beach.

The heat of the sun was still intense, even though it was late afternoon. The beach was deserted, a crescent of fine golden sand fringed by pines and lapped by the brilliant turquoise sea. When he stopped to plant the beach umbrella and dump their towels on the sand, Josh glanced up at her as she discarded the sage and white pareu she'd worn for the walk down and exposed herself in the scraps of white Lycra which passed for her bikini. His gaze seemed to heat her skin more fiercely than the sun.

Or maybe that was just her own fevered imagination, she told herself severely, taking Zoey's hand and running to the sea. As she plunged into the contrasting cool of the water, and turned to glance back up the beach, she tried not to notice Josh's masculine perfection. A challenge in itself, she reflected wryly. His dark body was gloriously virile and athletic in red Bermuda swimming-shorts. His legs were long and strongly muscled, rough with black hair. His shoulders, chest and abdomen were all healthily contoured and athletic, his muscles rippling as he moved. He was, quite simply, indecently gorgeous. Annie felt her stomach hollow with love and despair.

She expected Josh to fetch the windsurfing equipment, which was kept on the lowest slope of the hillside, under the trees. Instead he joined them in the shallows, and embarked on a riotous game of lifting Zoey into the air high above his head, lowering her onto his shoulders, and then throwing her, shrieking with pleasure, into the water. After a few minutes of unremitting merriment, Zoey declared that it was Annie's turn.

Her smile fixed, Annie glanced at Josh, alarmed to see the glitter of amusement in his eyes. Slicking his wet black hair from his face, he eyed her slim, tanned figure in the skimpy white bikini with comical appraisal.

'Would Annie like it, do you think?'

'Yes, yes!' Zoey clapped her hands in glee, jumping up and down in the sea in her bright blue swimming costume. 'Do it to Annie!'

'Traitorous infant... Josh, please, no; I'm warning you...'

She began to flounder away in the water, and felt Josh dive for her waist, bringing her down into the sea beside him, their wet bodies in close intimacy. He hauled her up against him, emerging with water streaming down his face and hair, the sun shimmering on the droplets. He looked like a pagan sea-god. The coarseness of his body hair was sensitising her wet skin. He laughed down at her, his teeth very white against his tan. She laughed at him helplessly, scooping handfuls of wet blonde hair from her face, trying and failing to control the inner shivers which had nothing to do with temperature.

'You don't weigh much,' he commented blithely, lifting her out of the water, twisting her easily in his arms and sitting her unceremoniously on his shoulders, astride his neck, 'but you sure wriggle a lot...'

'Oh, Josh...!' Half laughing now, she clung to his head, rocking perilously on her perch. He held her slender thighs to balance her, and the position she now found herself in felt so outrageous, she had no control over the shy, secret response she felt, with the briefest of bikini bottoms the only protection between intimate parts of her anatomy and the hard muscles of Josh's neck and shoulders. Then, with a shriek to rival Zoey's, she found herself tossed forward into the sea, and sinking beneath the surface. When she came up, he was laughing with Zoey, several feet away. She couldn't resist the urge to splash him with water in revenge. The ensuing water-fight was worthy of a couple of teenagers, she would reflect afterwards, vaguely ashamed of herself. Being set a rather poor example, Zoey joined in enthusiastically.

And when Josh put a stop to the fight by swimming over with a fast, powerful crawl, catching Annie and crushing her in his arms, their cool wet bodies triggered such heat between them that she burned for him in a way which made her quake with fearful longing…

'If you've overcome your physical aversion to me, there's still time to revise that pre-nuptial contract of marriage,' he murmured huskily into her ear, his fingers tracing the delicate hollow of her spine far enough down to splay sensuously over her buttocks and press her pelvis against his. She felt him hardening against her with a shock of panic. She froze in his arms. He released her slowly, and they stared at each other. His eyes looked the same deep, brilliant blue as the Aegean lapping around her waist. Beneath heavy lids, he read the withdrawal in her face and his expression grew shadowed again with cynical mockery.

'I gather you haven't?'

She glanced quickly to check that Zoey was safe; the child was happily engrossed in finding smooth white stones and piling them up at the water's edge.

'It's…it's not that I don't… I mean, sex would just complicate everything, Josh,' she said quickly, feeling her face getting hotter under that ruthless scrutiny. 'In the circumstances, we owe it to Zoey to…to stay on friendly terms. Don't you agree?'

'Meaning that if we started sleeping together we'd no longer be on friendly terms?'

'You know what I mean,' she said stiffly. 'Why do

you think platonic relationships last longer than sexual ones?'

He shrugged, his smile wry.

'Search me,' he said blandly, 'but I guess I'll have to play it your way, Annie. You're doing me the favour, after all…'

'Am I?'

'You know you are.' His eyes held a darker gleam, a warmth which made her catch her breath. His voice was huskier when he went on, 'I can't tell you how much it means to me, watching you with Zoey; she's like a different child already. You're perfect for her, Annie.'

'Josh, you don't have to thank me,' she said awkwardly. 'Zoey's very easy to love, you know, even when she's throwing a tantrum…'

He shook his head, his eyes holding hers, his rueful smile melting her. 'You're a special person, Annie. There's nothing easy about loving someone; it's a huge commitment. Some people never manage it.'

She stared at him, her throat dry.

'Josh, you're quite a special person too,' she told him lightly, in a voice that was not quite steady. 'Not many men I know would sacrifice their…their career and their freedom to rescue an orphaned three-year-old. I really admire you for what you're doing.'

There was a silence while he searched her face.

'We're both a couple of saints, then?' He grinned suddenly. 'Let's just hope our pious qualities allow us to make a go of our marriage. I still say you're getting the raw end of the deal.'

Only a few inches of water separated them, but it felt in that moment as if they were being held apart by an invisible barrier a mile wide.

'If it makes you feel better, Party Cooks has a few financial problems,' she pointed out as calmly as she could. 'Derrick told me before I came to Greece that my cash flow was looking a bit worrying. So, if you bail me out, you're doing me a favour too...'

'Derrick?'

She gazed at him unflinchingly.

'Derrick Butterford, my accountant...'

'He wouldn't be the legendary date, I suppose?'

'Well...' She caught her breath, grasping the dangerous lifeline. 'As a matter of fact, yes...'

Josh's eyes had narrowed to slits of aquamarine.

'So you're still involved with him?'

'Josh...' Her throat was as dry as dust. She swallowed, and tried again. 'I thought we agreed that our...our existing personal lives were our own business?'

'Right. So let me get this straight, once and for all.' His ruthless mockery belied his reasonable words, bewildering her and angering her at the same time. 'We're getting married, but who we see in our own time is our own affair. We're just...friends, and surrogate parents. And as far as our sexual needs are concerned, as long as Zoey doesn't get hurt we're both free to discreetly do our own thing. That's the agreement?'

She opened her mouth to speak and found that her voice had vanished. Josh's blue gaze seemed to flay her in the chilly silence which had fallen. Instead she nodded blindly and turned stiffly away. He caught her arm, holding her back.

'Is that truly what you want, Annie?'

'Isn't that the only way this marriage of ours could work?' she said expressionlessly. She carefully disengaged herself from his grip. Her mind was racing round in circles, trying to justify her feelings. Right from the start, Josh had made no secret of the fact that he found her physically desirable. She supposed his preoccupation with sex was understandable. He was male, after all. But how could she risk letting him make love to her? If she did that, he'd know how much she cared about him. She wouldn't be able to hide it...

And, without his love in return, she wouldn't be able to bear it. Better to keep things as they were.

Walking up the beach to gain the relative safety of her towel, she lay face down to sunbathe, with her sunhat tilted over her eyes to hide her turmoil...

'You always were secretive, Anoushka!' Liv accused laughingly, grabbing Annie for a private chat at the wedding reception, 'but this time you've really amazed everyone!'

They were in Josh's elegant Belgravia house, in the huge, plant-filled conservatory which led onto the kind of big, wild, rampantly informal garden Annie had always loved but never dreamed of owning in the centre of London. There were fruit trees and masses of old-fashioned pink and white climbing roses and secret benches and rope swings hidden in unexpected places. Josh had admitted that he employed a gardener to cultivate the wildness. He'd told her he'd always wanted an English country garden in the middle of a city.

Zoey was cavorting there happily with three recent converts to her fan club—boys aged seven and nine, offspring of Miles's married elder sister, and Meggie, already self-appointed surrogate big sister.

Liv's gaze was uncomfortably searching as she sipped her glass of champagne. 'You look as if you might have amazed yourself, Annie, darling. Are you happy?'

'I've just got married,' Annie pointed out calmly. Sitting back on the cane chair, she crossed her legs, smoothing the soft silk of her wedding dress with a slightly shaky hand. 'What do you think?'

Liv gazed at her for a moment, examining Annie's pale cheeks, the carefully arranged topknot of blonde hair with hardly a strand out of place, the classic, exquisite wedding dress of ivory silk, scoop-necked, long-sleeved and tight-waisted and falling in swirling gathers to the ankle, then let her eyes stray inside the house, scanning the crowded Regency dining-room.

'I don't know what I think.' Liv frowned faintly. 'You look like a fairy princess in that outfit, beautiful but remote. And I have a good memory, even if you don't! I can't forget our little chat at Miles and Alison's wedding—you vowed eternal spinsterhood and said you couldn't imagine trusting a man enough to let him trample on your deepest feelings.'

Annie was aware of the irony. In terms of not trusting the opposite sex, she'd met her match in Josh.

'Liv…'

'But one thing is for sure: Josh is the most smitten husband I've seen in a long, long time…'

Annie's eyes widened. She was about to make an acid retort when she remembered herself. She was saved from further testing by the arrival of her parents, and Miles and Alison—Alison pink with pleasure, cooing excited congratulations, her mother swooping over with arms outstretched, her father smiling his usual diffident, absent-minded smile.

'Anoushka, we're so happy for you, darling,' her mother announced, her dark eyes gleaming as she assessed her eldest daughter's appearance. 'You're very naughty, springing this surprise on us. But we were thrilled when we heard. And I know Josh is the right man for you…'

Her father gave her a hug. 'Congratulations, my dear,' he said quietly. 'Be happy. That's all we ask…'

'What a wonderful house.' Alison was looking approvingly at their palatial surroundings, her wide gaze slightly starstruck. 'I've seen Josh so many times on the news. He's really quite famous. Great choice, Annie…!'

'I'm sure he'll be gratified to have your seal of approval,' Annie laughed.

Miles gave her a kiss and a wink.

'I reckon Josh is the one who's made the great choice of wife,' he said, grinning, 'I thought he'd never tie the knot; he seemed too cynical, a confirmed bachelor. If anyone can reform him it's our Annie here. Good luck, sweetheart... Come to dinner soon, both of you. Alison will ring you with a date!'

Annie felt her smile setting into a false rictus as she excused herself.

'Thanks...enjoy yourselves; I'd better go and see if Josh's family are okay...'

Most of Josh's family had received too little notice to be able to attend. They were represented by his father, an older version of Josh, a tall, quiet man in a navy suit, with warm blue eyes and iron-grey hair, and Camilla, a female version of Josh, stunning in red and white silk, who was there with her husband and little girl. The remainder had sent supportive-sounding letters of congratulations, with orders to visit at the earliest opportunity.

'At least, with the villas on Skiathos, most of your family have met most of mine at some point over the years,' Annie had said to Josh as they'd planned the last-minute guest list. 'One of my nightmares about weddings is warring factions of relatives, forming opposing camps on either side of the room! I did the catering for one where they started throwing trifle at each other!'

'In this case, we'll just have the warring bride and groom throwing insults at each other,' Josh had quipped, his expression deadpan.

She was starting to wilt as she dutifully circulated. Apart from family, there were friends to face, all eager to tease and quiz her on the suddenness of the affair, her vow never to marry, and the mysterious inclusion of Zoey in the equation.

The hectic round of congratulations, encouragement, searching questions and joking ribaldry seemed never-ending. When Derrick Butterford appeared out of the crowd, tall and slim, sleek red-brown hair gleaming under the crystal chandelier, she was so exhausted by the effort of acting the euphoric bride that she returned his cool congratulations with a warmer hug and kiss than she'd intended.

'My felicitations, Annie,' he said, lifting his glass to her, his eyes flickering around, taking in the size and splendour of the house and grounds. 'Looks like you've pulled off quite a coup. When you had dinner with me just before you left for Greece, you didn't tell me this was what you had in mind.'

She eyed him warily. His tone was ambiguous, but she sensed buried hostility. Derrick's hazel eyes held a reproachful glint.

'I must confess I'd rather hoped, a couple of months ago, that I was in with a fighting chance.'

Trying to keep her voice light and her sense of humour intact, she managed a faint laugh. Liv had warned her about Derrick's apparent jealousy. She couldn't think where he'd got the idea that they were ever more than casual companions...

'Derrick, all we ever had was a...a friendship...' she began, in some astonishment.

'Friendship. What a lukewarm word that is. That was my mistake.' His voice had taken on a plaintive note. It occurred to her that he might have drunk quite a lot of champagne. 'I played the platonic game with you too long, didn't I, Annie?'

'Assuming I continue using your firm for financial advice, Derrick,' she said as evenly as she could, 'I'd like to feel that we could stay friends.'

'I'll claim a kiss to seal our friendship, then.' Catching her by surprise, he leaned forward, clasping her head in his hand and kissing her full on the mouth. Annie stood motionless, angry and embarrassed.

When Derrick let go of her, she saw Josh. He was watching them, tall and darkly attractive in his immaculate charcoal morning suit. She stared back at him helplessly from the other side of the room, through the groups of laughing, chattering people separating them. Her heart made a sickening lurch as she met his eyes.

Derrick was following her gaze. 'Whoops, new husband is glaring at us. Will he come and punch me on the nose, do you think? No, he's too deep in conversation with a very tasty redhead...'

Josh had turned away. He was talking to Veronica Whitton, who wore a black dress as if she were attending a funeral rather than a wedding.

She saw the other woman glance over, then say something to Josh and laugh, lifting one long white hand to his shoulder, reaching to whisper intimately in his ear.

'Excuse me, Derrick,' she said abruptly. 'I need some air...'

'Of course.' Derrick sounded smoothly complacent. 'You look pale, Annie. I'll come with you.'

'I'd really rather you didn't.'

'It's no trouble.' Derrick had a hand under her elbow and was steering her firmly out onto the lawn. 'What are old friends for?'

What indeed? she reflected furiously, shaking herself free of his hand and hurrying away from him to see Zoey and the other children. Gratified to find that Zoey was enjoying herself so much she hardly noticed her, Annie left her under the watchful eye of Josh's delightful Martha Betts and took a detour round the house to escape from Derrick. He was hovering near the conservatory, and stepped out to intercept her.

'Please don't let me keep you from the other guests, Derrick,' she said firmly. 'I need to check on something in the kitchen…'

'Okay, okay.' He grinned, following her like a persistent stray dog as she began to walk briskly towards the kitchen entrance. 'I get the message. Just direct me to the nearest bathroom before you run away?'

She left him in the back hall, made her way quickly towards the kitchen, then doubled back up the rear staircase and gained the safe haven of the main landing.

She darted into the master bedroom and slammed the door thankfully. Who would have thought Derrick had such an unpleasant side to his nature?

She leaned against the door until she'd controlled her desire to scream, and then walked across to the old pine four-poster bed. She slowly kicked off her delicate ivory leather high heels and sat down. This big bedroom— Josh's room—was directly opposite the room Josh was having redecorated specially for Zoey. With its restful, designer-faded peach and pale blue colour scheme, it was also where her possessions had been unpacked.

They'd agreed that, in case of any enquiries by the solicitors acting for Zoey's relatives, being seen to share a room was important. Josh had promised her the king-size bed to herself. He'd sleep in the adjoining dressing-room…

She caught sight of herself in the mirrored doors of a massive old pine wardrobe and felt dismayed. Her face looked white under her tan, her brown eyes shadowed in their sockets. No wonder Liv had been giving her such a disbelieving inspection. She hardly looked the radiant bride.

She didn't feel it, either. She felt emotionally drained. Today had been such an ordeal, half of her ecstatically happy, the other half desperately confused. The happy part had been Zoey's enjoyment, her thrill at wearing her new dress and her innocent excitement about the whole affair…and her own secret joy of knowing that, for whatever false reason, she was now Josh's wife…

Play-acting was exhausting, she decided miserably. She was suddenly so tired, she felt as if she could sleep for a month.

She released her hair from its neat coil, unbuttoned the tight bodice of her wedding dress, lay down and closed her eyes. If she just dozed for five minutes, she wouldn't be missed…

She was woken by the feel of the bed dipping at her side, and by Josh's voice, saying her name. Her eyes flew open, and she met Josh's narrowed blue gaze with a lurch of her heart.

'Hello, Mrs Isaac.'

Blinking dazedly, she stared up at him in silence for a few seconds. Was she imagining that his voice had sounded coldly angry?

'Hello, Mr Isaac,' she replied faintly. He looked so darkly attractive in the formal suit and white silk shirt he'd worn for the register office ceremony, she felt idiotically shy, conscious that her dress gaped open over her breasts, that the soft silk skirt had rumpled up around her legs as she slept.

'I gather you felt the desire to escape?'

'Oh, Lord…sorry! I fell asleep!' Her efforts to fasten her buttons again, to drag the skirt down to a more decent length, were defeated. She was suddenly all fingers and thumbs, and hot all over with embarrassment. She struggled to sit up, her hair tumbling over her eyes, finding herself very close to Josh, who made no effort to move. 'What time is it? I'll come back downstairs…'

'Don't bother; everyone's gone.'

His eyes were unreadable. She wasn't imagining it. There was something in his manner, something new, which made her heart begin to thud uncomfortably.

'Where's Zoey?'

'Safely with Martha, counting plastic ducks in the bath…'

'Thank heavens for Martha.' Annie smiled weakly. 'I'm not doing too well at surrogate motherhood so far, am I?'

'Zoey's fine. Throwing her weight around already.' His face softened fleetingly. 'Meggie and your cousin's boys have been invited by royal decree to stay the night.'

She stared at him, trying to work out the ominous glitter in his eyes, the trace of harshness in his voice. For the first time, she noticed a large silver tray on the long table at the foot of the bed. A bottle of champagne, two glasses, a cut-glass bowl of strawberries, a plate of caviare canapés… Josh must have brought this up for them both, she realised, bewildered at his arctic mood…

'Sorry…I know I shouldn't have left the reception like that. I didn't mean to be rude…I felt so shattered, I thought I'd grab five minutes' peace and quiet…

'Hey, it's okay,' he told her mockingly. 'By rights, you should be escaping on some romantic honeymoon now, shouldn't you? Aren't new brides entitled to find the whole thing an ordeal?'

'Maybe it's worse because I feel such a fraud…' she began, halting as she perceived the dangerous areas she was approaching.

'A fraud? In what way, Annie?'

'You know quite well what I mean,' she said flatly, running her hands over her tousled hair. 'Pretending to everyone that we've married for…for love…'

'I gather that's not what you pretended to Derrick Butterford?'

There was a charged silence. She stared at him.

'What do you mean?'

'That's a very impressive display of hurt innocence, Annie.'

Suddenly, despite the high ceiling, and the sunshine reflecting off the designer-faded peach of the walls, the room seemed cold. She shivered convulsively.

'Josh,' she began carefully, 'I'm afraid I don't know what you're talking about...'

His eyes hardened. He regarded her broodingly.

'I realise that we drew up a contract of marriage that allowed us our personal freedom, but I have to tell you, Annie, that not even in my wildest flights of imagination did I foresee you jumping into bed with someone else during our wedding reception.'

The blood drained from her face. Stiffly shifting her legs down from the bed, she stood up. He stood up too, blocking her way. She felt the heat of his body, he was so close. His expression was bleak. His eyes looked so dark, the blue had turned to ink-black.

'Is that what you think?' she managed. Her heart was thumping. She was angry, and she was also horrified to find that she was frightened; she might not be very well acquainted with the man she'd so rashly married, but this cold, accusing Josh was like a total stranger. It made the intimacy of their situation a thousand times more threatening.

'Are you going to deny it?' He spoke with bitter humour in his voice. Catching her shoulders, he gave her a slight shake. 'I met the guy only a moment or two ago. I was bringing you up some champagne, and he was coming down the back stairs! Then, when I thought about it, I saw him kissing you, and I saw the two of you going off together earlier. I'm not completely stupid, Annie...'

'Aren't you?' she whispered huskily. Tears were in her throat, stinging the backs of her eyes.

'He even had the nerve to make a snide remark about being a "very intimate friend" of yours as we met in the hall,' Josh ground out hoarsely. 'God, Annie, you might find me physically unacceptable, but believe it or not I was fool enough to hope…' He stopped, a flush of dark colour running along his cheekbones, and shook his head as if to clear his vision. 'God help me, I should have known better…'

'Known better than what?' Her voice was choked with fury. His touch was burning her.

'I should have known better than to think you were any different from the rest of them.'

She was shaken by the depth of her anger.

'You are unbelievable,' she said slowly, her voice ragged, her eyes over-bright as she held his gaze, 'and I must be out of my mind. I married you today thinking I could handle your…your jealousy, and your mistrust, and your cynicism, Josh…'

He gave a short, hoarse laugh.

'So what are you saying, Annie? It's all off? Within a few hours of saying "I do"?'

'No…I don't know…I just don't know…' Her voice caught on a sob. 'Josh, I didn't sleep with Phoenix and I didn't sleep with Derrick,' she whispered bitterly, 'but if you can't see the truth that's staring you in the face, then I don't know if we can have any kind of future together. Not if you're accusing me of sleeping with another man on our wedding day!'

CHAPTER EIGHT

THEY stared at each other in smouldering silence. The furious pain in Josh's eyes seemed to mirror Annie's own agony.

'Think about it, Josh! What kind of person would act like that?' she persisted, with soft vehemence. 'Would that be the kind of person you'd want to take care of Zoey? Can't you see that not all females are going to betray you? Just because your mother did?'

He flushed darkly.

'Let's leave my blasted mother out of this. You say the truth is staring me in the face. Well, I have a problem seeing it. So tell me, Annie, what is the truth?' he bit out softly. 'You tell me. What kind of a person are you?'

'I'm just human, like you,' she flung at him raggedly, gulping back the tears. 'I'm not perfect, but I'm not callous, or two-faced, or promiscuous, and if you were any sort of...of friend...if you weren't so eaten up with mistrust...you'd know that without being told. What's wrong with you, Josh?'

'What's wrong with me? I'm going crazy, that's what's wrong with me,' he groaned roughly. 'I know what we agreed in Skiathos, but I can't hack this open marriage thing, Annie...'

'Why?' she lashed back in bitter mockery. 'It was entirely your idea, remember? As long as we consider Zoey's needs first, we're free to seek our sexual satisfaction elsewhere. Your own words, Josh!'

Even as she repeated them, she felt sick. The thought of Josh making love to another woman made her feel eaten up inside. But that was her secret. She couldn't help the way she felt about him; she couldn't stop herself from loving him. He didn't have the same excuse. He'd made that perfectly clear. He'd said himself that emotional commitment was out of the question...

'You know how I feel about you,' he muttered huskily.

Her heart seemed to stop for a few seconds. Her mouth felt suddenly dry.

'Do I, Josh?'

He breathed in deeply. 'I find you sexy as hell,' he threw back at her, his eyes black with passion, 'but it seems like I'm the only male alive who doesn't get to sample your favours...'

The blood drained from her face. Pain was lancing through her.

'This is hopeless,' she breathed in a choked voice. 'You don't even listen to me. Even when I spell it out to you. I told you I didn't sleep with Derrick, and I didn't sleep with Phoenix either, but it doesn't make any difference, does it? You just believe what you want to believe, Josh.'

He was breathing unevenly, his eyes burning into hers.

'Okay, if you want the blunt truth, I'm jealous,' he said through his teeth. His face was a bleak mask, dark and contorted with suppressed anger. 'It's an unfortunate effect you have on me, Annie. That summer, in Skiathos, when I saw another guy climbing in your bedroom window, I felt like you'd kicked me in the teeth...'

'Oh, Josh...' She was trembling suddenly. Hearing the blazing sincerity in his voice was confusing and arousing and tormenting all at the same time.

'I'd started to feel we had something special going between us that summer,' he went on, as if the words were torn from him.

'Me too...' she whispered. 'And then you ruined ev-

erything, Josh. Just like you're ruining everything
now…'

'What am I ruining now? A happy marriage made in
heaven, Annie?'

'You're ruining any chance of getting our relationship
onto a level where we trust each other!' she shot back,
on a choked sob. 'Can't you see what you're doing? I'm
guilty until proved innocent every time, aren't I?'

Blindly, she made to push past him, and instead found
herself captured and dragged into his arms.

'Annie, God help me…' his voice shook '…this is
madness. Jealousy doesn't usually hit me this hard. If
I'm behaving like a goddamn caveman I can't seem to
help it where you're concerned…you drive me beyond
reason…I want you so badly…'

'Do you?' Tears stung her eyes and she blinked them
away. She began to shudder in his arms as she fought
to control her emotions.

'As if you didn't know by now…' His voice had deep-
ened with husky remorse. She took a snatched, faltering
breath. Held in the heat of Josh's arms, she could feel
his heart pounding violently against her breasts. Her eyes
were blurred with tears but she searched the fierce blue
gaze holding hers…

'Well, I'm your wife now, aren't I? Go ahead, have
me…' Her voice was a cracked, furious whisper. With
trembling hands, she pushed herself free of his embrace,
then fumbled with the fastening of her dress, ripping the
buttons open at her breasts, letting the soft silk slither
down to the floor. She stood in front of him, heart
pounding, wearing the cream lacy underwear, suspenders
and pale stockings she'd worn for their wedding ceremony.

Motionless as a statue, he stared at her, his eyes darkening in the taut mask of his face. He looked like a fallen

Greek god, she thought fleetingly—proud and austere and tormented by demons…

'Well?' she whispered defiantly. 'I'm all yours, Josh. What are you waiting for? Have you changed your mind now?' The tears welled in spite of her efforts to prevent them, and began to roll down her cheeks.

He said an unrepeatable word under his breath, and stepped forward to pull her back into his arms.

He held her there against him, one hand in her hair. He was breathing unevenly, his body taut as a coiled spring against her. The warmth of his chest burned her through the fine silk of his shirt. Her breasts seemed to swell against him in the confines of the white lace.

'Annie, don't cry…please, darling, don't cry…' The grim, suppressed tenderness in his voice made her insides melt with traitorous emotion. His arms gentling around her, he cupped her face, sought her lips with his, kissing her with hungry, bitter-sweet passion, the fire in his body suffusing her own body with answering fire. Abruptly, the heat between them flickered and flared into flames of desire so intense that she clung to him, dizzy and helpless in the conflagration which began to consume them both.

She was hardly aware of how she came to be on the bed, with Josh's warmth trapping her there, his long, hard, loose-muscled body driving all rational thought from her brain. The sensations he aroused in her were shockingly potent. Annie gasped, her fists clenching and unclenching helplessly, before she wrapped her arms round his strong back and instinctively arched her body closer.

The dazed hunger she'd felt that night in her flat, when they'd come within moments of making love, was back, a hundred times more powerful. She was lost, drowning in bewildering languor, all doubts gone. She tossed and writhed under his hands as he stroked and explored her body. He'd dispensed with his own clothes, flinging them impatiently to the floor, and now he was undressing her. She was dimly aware, in the dark heat of passion, that he was unfastening the soft lace basque, unhooking the suspenders, peeling down the fine cream stockings, and then the matching scrap of lacy panties.

Her eyes flew open as the last shred of covering was removed. She was completely naked with him, for the first time. She felt achingly vulnerable. His hooded gaze moved slowly over the rounded curve of her breasts, then lower to the smooth plane of her stomach, the slim swell of her hips, the fluff of blonde hair at the juncture of her slender thighs.

'You're beautiful,' he breathed huskily. 'So beautiful, Annie…'

But only on the outside, a buried voice said in her head. Inside you think I'm immoral and treacherous and unworthy of trust. The thought came and went, too over-shadowed by the shivers of desire to give her strength to resist.

His warm hands smoothed and explored with relent-less possession, following the route his eyes had just taken, skimming the softness of her breasts, lingering on the tight points of her nipples, then tracing down her ribcage to the smallness of her waist, the flatness of her stomach.

He stroked the length of her silken inner thighs with bold, demanding movements, sending her temperature rocketing as he lowered his head to kiss her body in shattering intimacy, his tongue seeking and tasting, and when his tongue finally flickered and focused on the very centre of her femininity she cried out loud, hardly re-cognising the sound of her voice. He slowly levered himself up, straddling her body. She opened her eyes to stare at him blindly; his black hair was tousled, his eyes shadowed with desire, his gaze narrowed darkly on her dazed face.

'Annie…sweetheart, say you want me. I need to hear you say it…'

The thick emotion in his voice was her final undoing. With a small, muffled moan of desire, she found herself arching and writhing beneath him, delicately opening herself to him, words failing her as her need for him ignited ever more fiercely. He moved his body, brushing his full length against her, and she felt the hard weight of his maleness against her stomach with a shock that felt like a thousand volts.

Even while her brain preached caution, the swelling, budding, fiery need filled her whole body. In a haze, she reached shaky hands to touch his face, moulding the hard cheekbones, the firm jaw, her fingers trembling for him, all resistance gone.

'I want you…' Her whisper was dragged from her lips, her eyes closed, melting sensuously beneath the long, muscular weight of him. 'I do want you, Josh…'

'Oh, baby… ' His deep voice was almost incoherent. He was raining quick, hungry kisses over her face, and neck, returning to her mouth like a man dying of thirst, drinking from her lips. Sending electric sensations shivering down her spine, his hands moulded her body in long, reassuring strokes from her breasts to her hips, and then he captured her thighs to force a place for himself, his hardness probing the tight, hidden moistness between the feminine curls. She arched instinctively against him, and with a hoarse groan he thrust hard and deep, in a bold, fierce act of possession…

Annie gave a muffled shriek. It was cut short by Josh's mouth covering her own, forcing her protests back into her throat. Idiotically, when she'd kept her own counsel for so long, she now began to struggle in blind panic. Stubborn pride had kept her silent until now.

But nothing—nothing she'd heard, or read, or seen so far—had warned her of this mortifying switch from pleasure to pain, this immense confusion of hard male flesh with delicate female...

Josh had stopped moving. The tight resistance he'd encountered made him freeze, levering back an inch or so to stare into her white, tense face.

'I don't believe this...' he began huskily. 'Annie...oh, God help me, Annie, darling...'

'I'm not sure I know how things go from here...' she whispered with agonised candour. 'Should...should it hurt, Josh...?'

'Sweetheart, no—hell, no!' His voice was unsteady, but there was a hint of suppressed anger, mixed up with the strain of controlling his desire. Was he angry with her, or with himself? 'You're a virgin? Oh, Annie, darling, Annie, are you crazy? Why didn't you tell me?'

He cradled her in his arms, crushing her possessively along the length of his body, the pounding of their hearts echoing between them, and she felt some of the fear and pain receding, and a lot of the previous warm, wonderful sensations taking over again. She moved, with unconscious provocation, beneath him, and felt his body tense instantly as powerful desire raged through him.

'I think it's all right now...' she whispered in a stifled voice, shivery with emotion.

'You think so?' His ragged response sounded ambiguous, but she was too dizzy with love and desire to delve for hidden meanings, and Josh was reaching down to ease her trembling legs around his waist, one skilful hand moving between their bodies to seek the throbbing bud of passion at her apex; she was so strung up with desire and emotion, his first touch made her catch her breath as a new, intense sensation took her by surprise, spreading from that one fiery point and spinning wildly out to every nerve-ending in her body, like sparks from a Catherine wheel.

'Oh…' She caught her breath, gasped frantically for air, clutching him in unbearable excitement. 'Yes… oh…!'

'Definitely all right…' he breathed roughly, and then, with a raw, shuddering groan, he withdrew from the tight, throbbing union and thrust inside her again, and again—his whole body rigid with a spasm which racked him so explosively, she shut her eyes and dug her nails into his shoulders and rode out the faintest traces of pain until it became a secret, vanquished pleasure, and she found herself sobbing his name, over and over, all inhibitions gone, her voice cracked and broken with emotion…

Her first, cataclysmic sexual experience had left a confusing mixture of after-effects, she decided. She felt totally boneless, wiped out, but at the same time she was glowing all over with the wonder and joy of how Josh had made her feel. She ran her mind tentatively over her body, trying to analyse how she did feel, exactly. As if she'd been crushed by a steamroller, then put through a mangle and then, deliciously, sensuously, lovingly, put back together again. She was euphorically happy and oddly apprehensive, as if there was a hidden catch she'd almost forgotten, waiting to pounce on her when she regained her senses…

Was this how making love always felt? she wondered dazedly.

She became aware that she'd lost the warm security of Josh's arms. He'd released her, and was lying flat on his back, his profile taut and forbidding when she risked a sideways glance. And then reality came back with a cold shock to her system. She should have told him, she realised despairingly. She shouldn't have kept her virginity a secret…

When she tried to sit up, Josh reached an arm across and held her still. He rolled over so that she was half trapped beneath him. He leaned up on one elbow to inspect her flushed face.

'Aren't I allowed to move?' she queried.

'Not just yet,' he told her, his smoky blue eyes unreadable. 'Annie…sweetheart, are you okay?'

'Yes, I'm fine,' she told him cautiously.

'Why the hell didn't you tell me you were a virgin?' he demanded huskily, a hint of suppressed anger shaking his voice. 'I hurt you. That was the last thing I'd ever have wanted to do, Annie. If you'd told me the truth…'

'Josh, is this going to be the unwritten rule of our marriage?' she countered unsteadily. 'That whatever happens I always get the blame?'

'Annie…'

'What was the point in my telling you the truth?' she heard herself saying raggedly. 'Why should I have expected you to believe me? Don't make me feel guilty for not telling you the truth in this particular instance, Josh. You insult my morals and my pride…and then blame me for not telling you that…that…'

'That I was venturing into uncharted territory?' he supplied grimly. His eyes were very brilliant under heavy lids as he held her gaze. 'You must admit, it was a fairly important piece of information…'

'You could have asked,' she suggested, quivering with indignation. 'Why should you have assumed I wasn't a virgin? Oh, of course, I remember. Because you were so convinced I'd slept around all over the place! How do you think that makes me feel?'

Josh raked a shaky hand through his hair.

'It feels like I spend my whole life apologising to you, Annie. Saying I'm sorry isn't enough, is it?'

'Saying sorry won't undo what just happened, will it?'

She hadn't meant to say that, she realised, even as the surge of pride and resentment made her choke the angry words out. She didn't want to undo what they'd just done. How could she be sorry that Josh had been her first lover? His lovemaking had been physically unforgettable, and he'd been gentle and wonderful when he'd found out it was her first time. No, she wasn't sorry it had happened. Even if he didn't actually love her, he'd made her feel as if he did, just for those few ecstatic minutes.

But this cool, wary post-mortem wasn't how she'd imagined it might be like afterwards, how she'd promised herself it would be. In her secret imagination she'd pictured her first lover fiercely declaring his love for her, overwhelming her with tender possessiveness, promising he'd always love her. Josh wasn't going to tell her he loved her. And right now she was shattered by how strongly she yearned to hear those words from him, longed for them so badly, her heart felt as if it was physically aching...

Josh's eyes were bleak on hers.

'Was it so bad for you, Annie? Are you regretting it already? Are you sorry it happened?'

'What do you think?' She bit her lip, hating herself for her defensiveness. This was dreadful. Making love with Josh had felt as if it might be healing this gaping wound in their relationship. Now this bitter verbal aftermath was driving them further apart. She felt as if her brief, fragile vision of a closer rapport with Josh was literally crashing down around her ears.

'I'm sad that you feel that way—' his voice was hoarse with emotion '—but I guess I can't blame you.' With one swift, athletic movement he stood up and disappeared into the bathroom, coming out a few moments later wearing a dark blue towelling robe, and carrying another in his hand.

'Here.' He eyed her bleakly, handing the robe to her. 'Put this on, Annie. You're shivering. I don't want to be responsible for you catching double pneumonia on our wedding day. Can I tempt you to a glass of champagne? Strawberries? Caviare?'

She shook her head, hating the bitter self-mockery in his voice. She slowly took the robe and shrugged it on, then slid off the bed and stood there in frozen misery, feeling the gulf widen between them. The contents of the silver tray seemed to mock her with an air of carefree celebration.

'Why were you so determined to believe I'd slept with Phoenix, and then with Derrick?' she demanded huskily. 'How could you imagine, even for one moment, that I'd be so self-centred and…and deceitful…?'

There was a taut silence.

'Well, I guess I'm just a mean, suspicious bastard…' He shrugged, his face expressionless. 'But I've paid for it now, haven't I? Was it worth it, Annie?'

'Was what worth it?'

'Sacrificing your innocence in the pursuit of justice,' he said softly.

She stared at him in mounting misery.

'What are you talking about?'

'It's just occurred to me why, at no small cost to yourself, you let me go crashing in where no man had gone before,' he explained wryly.

'Well, maybe you'd like to enlighten me?'

'Revenge. For misjudging you. For the pain I've caused you.'

'Revenge?' she managed to repeat, white-faced with misery.

'Can you deny it? Hell, sweetheart, I can't blame you. I deserve it. All this time, you kept secret the one piece of proof that would convince me without a shadow of doubt that I was wrong to mistrust you.' His gaze was heavy-lidded, his expression bitterly self-mocking. 'All this time, you've given me more and more rope to hang myself. The perfect punishment...'

'Well, that really is ironic, Josh,' she began in a hoarse, strangled voice, 'because even if what you say is true it could hardly be called a perfect punishment, could it?'

'No?'

'No! A perfect punishment presumably deters the wrongdoer from repeating the mistake?' she pointed out, clenching her fists at her sides. 'Whereas here you are, committing the same crime all over again!'

He stared at her in bleak silence.

'Instead of making an effort to put our relationship on a level where we trust each other, the first thing you do, when you've...you've taken my virginity, is accuse me of using it as a means of revenge! I can't win.'

Josh closed his eyes, let out a long, shuddering breath. He raked a tense hand through his hair.

'What the hell was I supposed to think?' he countered with quiet bleakness.

She stared at him, her eyes wide with pain.

'Anything, Josh! Anything but that! How do you think I feel now?'

'I'm not feeling too good about myself either, Annie.'

The bitter silence which fell seemed to go on for ever.

'Maybe it would be better if I had a room of my own,' she finally heard herself say woodenly. She could hardly believe she was saying these things. It was as if someone else were talking. As if another person had taken over her heart and mind, and smothered all the warmth and joy and tenderness she'd felt in Josh's arms...

He shook his head, his mouth hardening.

'Not until the courts have definitely ruled in our favour,' he said flatly. 'I told you I'd sleep in the dressing-room, Annie. If you care about Zoey, don't rock the boat at this stage.'

She let out a long, tremulous breath, and turned her back on him, hugging her arms round her chest. She felt as if she might be breaking into a thousand pieces, as if she had to physically hold herself together to stave off the disintegration.

'I don't see how anyone will know...'

'If anyone asks Zoey if her new mummy and daddy share the same bedroom, I want her to be able to say truthfully that they do. That part of our agreement is not negotiable, Annie.'

'No. Of course not. Zoey is the only important factor in this relationship. I hadn't forgotten that, Josh.' She swallowed abruptly, tears choking her throat.

'Right,' he said grimly. 'At least we've got one thing straight. As for the rest, don't worry, I'll just have to learn to live with my guilt, won't I? Come on, sweetheart.' His voice had softened a fraction, making her heart contract painfully. 'I'll run you a hot bath. Then I'll treat you to dinner at the best restaurant in town...'

She turned to look at him, wrestling with her pride. He felt guilty about his behaviour, and he felt sorry for her. It was unbearable...

'Josh, you don't have to do any of those things...' she began stiffly. 'And to be honest the last thing I feel like is going out to dinner...'

'Then I'll bring you supper on a tray, to eat in front of the TV.' He grinned bleakly. 'I'll even cook it myself. You never did try my spaghetti carbonara, did you? Annie, darling...' He came across to her, reached out a hand as if to take hers, then dropped it again quickly. A muscle twitched in his jaw as he watched her warily. 'Humour me—please? I may be a jealous, suspicious brute, but at least I'm perceptive enough to see where

I've caused maximum offence. If it helps at all I'd give anything to turn back the clock and do this differently. It can't have been your idea of a romantic honeymoon experience, losing your virginity to a sex-crazed animal...'

'Josh, it wasn't like that—' A lump in her throat was threatening to choke her.

'And the least I can do is behave like a civilised male from now on,' he cut in drily. 'Don't look so tragic,' he added, his voice roughening at the expression in her eyes. 'I won't touch you again. I'll be the soul of propriety, a total celibate. You'll see.'

He turned on his heel and went into the bathroom. She heard him turn on the taps, heard the comforting sound of the water running into the bath. He was acting like a stranger, she realised in sudden panic. A polite, helpful, courteous stranger. It was as if the shattering intimacy that had just taken place between them had never happened...

Any remaining delusions that she could sustain the play-acting over her relationship with Josh took a heavy knock over the next couple of weeks, and vanished completely at Miles and Alison's dinner party.

Her cousin and his wife, proud of their recently re-decorated house in Camden and eager to entertain as a married couple, had lost no time in issuing an invitation to Annie and Josh. Also invited were Liv plus a young blond man called James, currently doing casual work at Party Cooks and, by wonderful coincidence, enrolled for the same university course as Liv in the autumn.

Annie, already apprehensive over keeping up the pretence for a whole evening, in the face of another married couple's genuine devotion, and Liv's sparkling new romance, had spent much time soaking in the bath, washing her hair, agonising over what to wear. Clad in a short, morale-boosting silk dress in a soft shade of gold, with her make-up discreet and her hair in a neat topknot, she practised her most sociable smile as she got into the car. Josh, behind the wheel, in navy, pleat-waist trousers and an expensive-looking midnight-blue silk shirt, was politely detached and unreachable—the way he'd been since that fraught exchange on their wedding day.

They drove there in cool, tense silence, broken only by impersonal remarks about the arrangements for Zoey, who was being cared for by Martha. When they arrived, Annie was dismayed to find Veronica Whitton there. Miles and Veronica knew each other through their work as journalists, she remembered. But it was still a shock to find her, seductive in black satin, already comfortably ensconced in Miles and Alison's elegant sitting-room. She was accompanied by a tall, tanned man who struck Annie as a mere token escort, since Veronica spent the whole evening determinedly flirting with Josh.

'It's just so lovely,' Alison enthused to Annie, handing round after-dinner mints to follow a superb meal of salmon hollandaise and new potatoes, raspberry pavlova, and Stilton and grapes. 'Who would have thought that just a few weeks after Miles and I got married you and Josh would have a whirlwind romance, and get married and set up home with little Zoey, within easy reach of us?'

'Who indeed?' Veronica murmured, her green eyes flashing with dislike as she glanced at Annie. 'You're a dark horse, aren't you, Josh, darling?'

'As dark as they come,' he agreed civilly. He slowly drank some of his brandy, his face mask-like.

'How's married life suiting you, then, Annie?' Miles grinned, eyeing them both from the other end of the table. Liv and her new boyfriend, clearly very involved with each other, had excused themselves and wandered out into the garden, leaving the six of them sitting around the dining table. Miles and Alison appeared happily oblivious to the underlying tension in the atmosphere as Miles continued teasingly, 'You, little cousin, I'm told, were the one at my wedding implying that you didn't believe in love and marriage. A few weeks later, you're Mrs Josh Isaac. How did Josh manage to change your mind?'

'Oh…' Annie could feel her smile freezing '…you know, he just used his endless charm, his devastating personality, his sex appeal…'

'His bank balance?' Veronica put in slyly.

'Naturally,' Annie joked lightly, after a short, charged silence. 'That was definitely the deciding factor!'

'Annie promised to top it up when I'm an impoverished writer,' Josh put in smoothly. Annie caught his eye, with a reluctant pang of gratitude.

'I must say,' Alison was chipping in, gazing at Miles with a glow that proclaimed her love to the world, 'you journalists are hard nuts to crack; I thought Miles would never get around to popping the question. We'd be in a really romantic situation, and then his mobile phone would ring and he'd be dashing off in hot pursuit of the latest news!'

Thoughts of that moment during their fateful evening in her flat brought a flush of colour to Annie's cheeks. She dared not even look at Josh. But she could feel his amused gaze on her.

'Annie may have had a similar experience,' he murmured unforgivably. She felt her colour deepen to a truly embarrassing red, and clenched her hands in her lap, glad of the cover of laughter rippling round the dining table.

'Josh had a very jaundiced view of marriage last time we talked about it,' Veronica was saying, in a light, flippant tone which didn't quite mask her bitchiness. 'I must say, I'm very suspicious about all this unseemly haste.

But, of course, there is poor little orphaned Zoey. Personally I'd look no further for the motive...'

There was another brief, awkward silence.

'Zoey's predicament certainly was a motive for marriage,' Josh said, steel in his voice beneath the softly humorous tone. As Annie glanced at him in shock, he slid an arm around her shoulders, his fingers caressing the soft bare flesh of her upper arm. 'But I think Annie and I were both wary of commitment. We were just looking for a convenient excuse to hide behind. Zoey's tragedy did one good thing—it brought us together. Didn't it, sweetheart?'

Drawing her closer, he dropped a light, searching kiss on her mouth, stroking back a strand of hair with his hand. When he released her, the expression in his heavy-lidded eyes turned her limbs to jelly. Her whole body on fire, all she could do was sit there like a statue, hardly breathing. Liv, followed by her boyfriend, had come back into the room as Josh was speaking, and she was smiling knowingly at Annie as she came to sit at the table.

'Wow,' Alison murmured huskily, expelling her breath on a long sigh. 'My legs have gone all funny! Miles, make some more coffee, darling; I think some of our guests are anxious to get home to bed!'

The remainder of the evening was dominated by talk of Max's tragic death—since he'd also been a colleague of both Miles and Veronica—and of Zoey, and the recent happy outcome of the court case, in Josh's favour.

And then Annie went to the bathroom and bumped into Veronica as she came out. The redhead gave her a pitying look.

'Josh is looking a bit strained,' she murmured. 'Do you think the responsibilities of married life and instant parenthood are taking their toll?'

'Not that I'm aware of...' Annie began coolly.

'Still, when he came to my drinks party the other night he was more like his old self. Relaxed, witty, wonderful company. And he stayed on for ages after the rest of the guests had gone. Maybe he needs to get out more on his own? Sorry you couldn't make it, by the way, Annie. Another time, maybe?'

'I doubt it. Drinks parties aren't really my scene.' Annie kept a stiff social smile on her lips to mask the acute dislike she felt for Veronica, coupled with a cold, sinking void in her stomach. Josh had been to a party at Veronica's. He'd said nothing to her about it. Even though she'd feared their marriage was devoid of love and trust, this strong evidence of his continuing link with Veronica was a blow that was almost too painful to contemplate...

When they said their goodbyes, Alison hugged her and whispered that she was so glad Annie was happy. It made the cool, tense atmosphere in the car on the way home feel even more ironic than earlier.

'You missed your vocation,' she managed finally, when they were nearly home and the silence had become intolerable. 'You deserve an Oscar for that performance, Josh!'

'Thanks. I thought I did rather well.'

She stayed silent, her heart heavy, her stomach like lead. His glance was dark as he parked the car then came round to open her door.

'If you want me to demonstrate the real thing again, then you only have to say the word,' he said softly as they made their way to the front door.

'The real thing? Sex, you mean?' she shot back in a low, tense voice. 'That's the only bit of an adult relationship you can relate to, isn't it?'

'And you're the ultimate authority on adult relationships, I suppose?' he countered, catching her by the shoulder and jerking her round at the door, trapping her against the wall, his eyes very piercing as he searched her face. 'It never fails to amaze me how the woman who lavishes all that love and attention and patience and humour on Zoey can be the same woman who treats me with such self-righteous contempt whenever we're alone together.'

His nearness was unbearable. Holding her breath, she made herself stand very still. Any effort to push him away might trigger the familiar flashpoint of passion, and the risk of that was even more intolerable...

'I'm sorry,' she conceded stiffly. 'I had no idea that was how I seemed to be treating you. I...I must obviously make an effort to be more...amiable.'

'At least I can be grateful you don't take it out on Zoey.'

She caught her breath. In a choked voice she said, 'That's a horrible thing to say. I love Zoey; you know I do. I would never, ever be unkind to Zoey, or any other child for that matter...'

'So you admit you're being unkind to me?' he queried, with a short, derisive laugh.

'Let me go in, please, Josh. I'm tired; I'd like to go to bed...'

'Far be it from me to keep my adorable new wife from her big, lonely bed,' he said with weary resignation, releasing her abruptly and unlocking the front door. 'Nice seeing Miles and Alison so wrapped up in each other, wasn't it?'

'Very nice. Liv seems very taken with her new boyfriend, too,' Annie agreed woodenly. 'I'm really pleased for her. She's been very...wary of the opposite sex for quite a while now. It seems the whole world is full of people genuinely in love with each other. What a pity you and Veronica didn't make a go of it. She's blatantly infatuated with you...'

There was a moment's electric silence.

'What the hell are you talking about, Annie?'

'Don't act amazed and innocent,' she said shakily. 'It's obvious to me that she's the one you'd be with if it wasn't for Zoey.'

'Annie, you know nothing about my relationship with Veronica Whitton,' Josh said with dangerous calm. 'We've barely even discussed the wretched woman...'

'I'm not surprised. You obviously prefer to keep your relationship with her strictly private. You went to her drinks do without even telling me.'

'Did she tell you that tonight?' His eyes had darkened on her stricken face.

'Yes.'

'Annie, that was a business thing,' he said slowly. 'You wouldn't have known anyone there. I couldn't see any point in asking you...'

'Don't bother making excuses. Actions speak louder than words, don't they? Goodnight, Josh. Thanks for at least saving face tonight.'

'Any time, Annie.' He stood in the hall, watching her as she half ran up the stairs to her room. His cool, despairing tone still echoed in her ears as she climbed miserably into bed ten minutes later. And, as she tried to get to sleep, all she could see when she closed her eyes was Veronica's possessive green gaze across the dinner table, following Josh's every move...

'I have to fly to Cambodia.' Josh made the announcement at breakfast three weeks later, from behind a copy of the newspaper.

Annie paused in the act of buttering another slice of toast for Zoey. Her stomach had clenched involuntarily.

'I thought you'd stopped working for Reuters...?' The polite, calmly distant tone she used was the one she'd got used to using with him.

'This is research for my book,' he explained coolly,

lowering the broadsheet and meeting her eyes with a level blue gaze. 'I need to verify the current rumours of unrest out there.'

'Surely, with all your contacts in the foreign news line…'

'There's no substitute for firsthand experience.'

Annie fiddled with her sleeveless cream cotton overshirt, smoothing it down over her short sage linen skirt.

Folding the paper, Josh reached for the coffee pot. 'Do you want coffee?'

'No…thanks. I'm drinking tea this morning.' She pushed her slice of dry toast around her plate, and watched him pouring the hot liquid into his own cup, her sense of smell recoiling at the aroma she'd once found appetising.

She had some kind of virus, she'd privately decided. Probably a return of that stress-related thing she'd had at Miles and Alison's wedding, when she'd nearly fainted. Certainly the stress of this ill-judged marriage to Josh was taking its toll. A vague feeling of queasiness seemed to have lingered now for the last couple of days.

Thank heavens she still had her business to take her mind off everything. She'd evolved a satisfactory routine which fitted in with Zoey's needs, working every morning until she collected Zoey from her playgroup at lunchtime. She then devoted afternoons to spending time with Zoey, either in the garden or in the kitchen—the little girl was rapidly developing a passion for picking endless bunches of flowers to give to people who dropped by to see them, and baking scones and fairy cakes to be devoured at teatime in front of children's television…

She ran her fingers distractedly through her hair and gazed out of the conservatory windows at the garden, in muted confusion.

'When are you going?' she managed finally.

'Tonight.'

'Tonight?' Her unguarded reaction hung in the air, and she bit her lip, furious with herself.

'I'll only be gone four or five days.' He was gazing at her closely, adding quietly, 'Are you all right, Annie? You look a bit peaky.'

'Perfectly all right, thanks.' She dropped her eyes from that searching dark blue gaze. She was aware that Zoey was avidly listening to their conversation.

Zoey took a huge bite of her toast, and spoke with her mouth full.

'I want to come too!'

'Not this time, honeybunch. But if you're a really good girl for Annie I'll bring you back a present.'

'You'll return via a certain little boutique?' Annie murmured, unable to suppress a quick smile.

'Maybe.' Josh's answering smile was fleeting, a flash of white teeth in his dark face. When it vanished, faded to a cool, watchful mask, she felt all the more bereft and isolated in this empty shell of a marriage.

Josh had kept his promise—he'd kept his distance, physically; he came to bed much later than she did, and rose very early to go for a jog, then for a swim at the health club he belonged to, coming back to take Zoey to the playgroup which was attached to the primary school she'd be attending in the autumn, before settling down to work on his book in the study. He used another bathroom down the landing. He went in and out of the dressing-room by an outer door. She hardly saw him.

'Why can't I come?' Zoey persisted, dark eyes beginning to fill with tears.

'Because Annie will be lonely here on her own,' Josh told the little girl solemnly. He leaned back in his chair, pushing his black hair from his forehead. The action drew attention to his body. Annie tried not to notice how good that body looked, lean and attractive, broad-shouldered and lean-hipped, supple, athletic muscle moving beneath the white T-shirt and tight Levis.

'No, she won't; she's got Martha, and Aunty Livvy and Granny and Grandpa and Uncle Miles and Aunty Alison and Meggie and—'

'Well, I'm going to be very busy in Cambodia, doing things little girls don't like doing,' Josh tried again.

'What things?'

'Er…travelling, talking to lots of boring people…' Josh floundered a little, catching Annie's eye with a hunted look. She felt her lips twitch, in spite of her inner misgivings.

'Anyway, we'll be having fun here,' she told Zoey firmly, pouring her more orange juice and handing it to her. 'We're going to Cornwall to the seaside; we're going to see Granny and Grandpa and Meggie,' she finished up, mentally reviewing her commitments for Party Cooks and thanking the gods that her new, generous staffing levels could cope with such impromptu arrangements.

'Thanks for that,' Josh told her later, when Zoey had disappeared happily to the kitchen to help Martha make pastry, and regale her with the news of her forthcoming trip to the seaside. 'I'll try to keep research trips to a minimum… I wouldn't go if I didn't think it was vital to my current plot…'

'You don't have to explain anything to me,' she said coolly. 'You'll probably find it's in your blood, anyway—flying off to dangerous locations. Maybe you'll find you can never give it up…'

'Annie…' He caught her arm as she began to leave the room. Electric shocks zigzagged through her nervous system. Going very still, she raised her eyebrows enquiringly.

'What is it?'

'Come outside for a moment. I want to talk to you.'

She looked up at him, suddenly aware of his nearness, of the hypnotic blue of his eyes, of the catastrophic effect he had on her, her heart contracting in panic.

'What about?'

He was leading her out of the conservatory, where they'd been having breakfast, with gentle but firm insistence. Halfway down the sweep of lawn there was an old wooden table and slatted wooden chairs. The July morning was warm, slightly overcast, and the scent of the nearby pink climbing rose was sweet and strong.

'So?' she challenged squarely, sitting on one of the chairs. 'What are we talking about, Josh?'

'About you.'

'Oh?' Suddenly her heart was pounding harder than it had been.

'We've hardly exchanged more than half a dozen words recently,' he said bleakly, 'but I feel obliged to ask if everything is…all right with you, Annie.'

'What?' Her stomach had hollowed, her heart was sinking.

'I know I swore I wouldn't touch you again, but that doesn't mean I don't take full responsibility for what happened on our wedding day, Annie. I just need to know…'

He stopped at the coldly discouraging expression in her eyes. Hitching lean, denim-clad hips against the table, he crossed his arms over his chest, his expression hunted.

'I feel, in the circumstances,' he finished up on a huskier, harder note, 'that it would be remiss of me not to enquire if you're pregnant, Annie.'

She was white with shock.

'Pregnant?' she repeated idiotically. 'Are you crazy? Of course I'm not pregnant! Of all the stupid things to ask…'

Josh's dark eyebrow arched mockingly.

'Not so stupid,' he said gently. 'For my sins, I used no protection, Annie. And, unless I'm very much mistaken, you weren't on the pill, or using any other contraceptive device.'

The colour had come back to her face now, burning her cheeks.

'For heaven's sake, just because one has...has unprotected sex once, a baby doesn't automatically follow, Josh!' she said in a small, stiff voice. 'I'm surprised you could be so...naive.'

His dark face blanched slightly.

'That's not something I'm accused of too often. I wouldn't ask if I hadn't noticed some familiar signs,' he persisted, his voice now as cold as hers. 'I have two sisters, both of whom have children. In the early days of pregnancy, they both took an abrupt dislike to coffee, they both took on that slightly bleached-out appearance. However, if you're not pregnant, that's that. End of problem.'

Something buried deep in Annie's subconscious let out a silent howl of pain.

'Problem?' she challenged. 'Since when have babies conceived in holy wedlock been seen as a problem, Josh?'

Josh's gaze grew heavier, his blue eyes darker. Annie was suddenly reminded of how seldom Josh actually lost his temper. Watching him now, he looked disconcertingly close to doing so.

'They're only a problem if they're conceived in a marriage as arid and lacking in affection as ours is proving to be, Annie.'

'I wasn't aware that you'd ever expected anything else,' she reminded him, her voice tense with suppressed emotion. 'If you're desperate for affection you can always go to another of Veronica's parties...'

She wished, instantly, that she hadn't said it. Recently,

pride had driven her to say things she didn't mean—to say the very opposite of what she meant, in fact. No wonder it was listed as one of the seven deadly sins, she reflected miserably.

Josh reacted as if she'd physically hit him. He straightened up, thrusting both hands through his black hair with a quick, forceful, impatient gesture.

'I've been thinking,' he said decisively. 'We can't go on like this. It's not fair on you, nor on me, and in the long run I doubt if it's fair on Zoey…'

She felt a rush of fear, like a cold hand on her heart. Everything abruptly seemed unreal: the garden where she sat with the morning sun on her back, the conversation she and Josh were having…

'What are you trying to say?'

'The custody challenge is over now. Once the adoption is legally done and dusted, Annie, I suggest we see our solicitors again about this fragile sham of a marriage. Zoey's still very young. It would be traumatic for her at any age, but some say the younger the child, the less damage is done in the long term.'

'Josh…' her voice shook with unwelcome emotion '…what are you talking about?'

'What the hell do you think I'm talking about?' he said bitterly. 'I'm talking about putting an end to this travesty of being happy newly-weds. We seem to be doomed to make each other miserable, don't we? Even though it's the last thing I want, I'm talking about getting a divorce, Annie.'

CHAPTER NINE

THE distraction of the visit to Cornwall was short-lived. Zoey seemed to like the beach and sea and the comfortable, homely, family feel of the Rectory, but she fretted for Josh. He rang once, as he'd said he would, confirming his safe arrival and talking briefly to Zoey. But Annie privately wondered if the well-intentioned telephone call, emphasising Josh's absence in a faraway place, had been a mistake. The next two nights, the little girl woke screaming, sobbing first for her daddy and then for Josh. After anxious consultations with her mother, Annie decided that taking Zoey back to London was the only way to restore the missing sense of security.

Added to this, Annie had a nagging anxiety of her own, on top of Josh's shattering talk of divorce. His thoughtful enquiry about the possible repercussions of their wedding day had made her feel incredibly stupid because, after a quick visit to the chemist and a small personal test in the privacy of the bathroom, Josh's suspicions appeared to be confirmed.

She sat in the bathroom, stared at the tell-tale blue circle in the test-tube, and tingled with a bewildering mixture of emotions: fear, excitement, disbelief. Could she really be pregnant? Could she really be expecting Josh's baby? She wanted to hug herself with happiness and weep for the irony of it...

But there could still be some kind of mistake, couldn't there? How reliable were these home tests? she wondered, her mood swinging from elation to anxiety.

Back in London, she saw her doctor, who confirmed the home-test result. The euphoria triggered by this news

167

lasted about two minutes. After that, a sense of reality took over. Josh would have to know, of course. The sooner the better. He'd indicated that pregnancy was a problem, too bad. Since he'd spoken as if divorce was what he wanted, so be it. Whatever the circumstances of its conception, this would be her baby, whether Josh wanted to be involved or not…

Here, her defiant train of thought came to an abrupt halt. If she was trying to convince herself that this was true, she was failing spectacularly. This baby wouldn't only be hers; she couldn't exist in a vacuum and pretend that it didn't have a right to know its father. Babies grew into children—vulnerable, enquiring little children like Zoey. Her baby was also Josh's baby, and it was entitled to both of them as its parents. And the implications were wider still, because her baby would be a little brother or sister for Zoey. From the envious comments Zoey had made about friends at the playgroup with little brothers or sisters or new babies in their families, Annie had no doubt that Zoey would be overjoyed at the news…

Reality hit her like a physical blow. Josh wanted a divorce. But divorce wasn't what she wanted, was it? It was the last thing *she* wanted. She wanted, more than anything in the world, to stay married to Josh, but for it to be a real marriage, with a husband who loved her as much as she loved him. She wanted someone to wave a magic wand over their relationship and transform it into a loving partnership, so that they could bring up their baby and Zoey in a warm, loving, family atmosphere, like the atmosphere she'd been lucky enough to grow up in herself…

The trouble was, with the way her relationship with Josh had deteriorated since their wedding day, she had no idea how to achieve such an ideal. It took love to build a marriage like that. But surely it had to be a two-way thing. Josh might not love her but, if she was completely honest, he'd shown a gentleness and a genuine concern for her welfare on numerous occasions. He could be kind and caring. Maybe that would be enough. Maybe she'd just have to swallow her pride and see...

She was suddenly desperate to talk to him, to hear his voice. In growing impatience, she waited for him to ring again. He didn't. Instead, as if to torture her, the ten o'clock news dwelt at some length on the current unrest in Cambodia.

There was grave talk of kidnappings and abductions and she felt a cold twist of premonition in her heart. In desperation, she tried to telephone Josh at the number he'd given her. She couldn't get through.

The deadline for Josh's return came and went. Five days turned to six. The twist of premonition turned to an icy foreboding. Annie deliberately threw herself into her work, and went through the familiar routines with Zoey, careful to say nothing in front of the little girl, trying to keep a determinedly cheerful face, but in the end she could stand the agony no longer and consulted Miles.

'Don't worry about Josh,' her cousin reassured her, hearing and correctly interpreting the crack of anguish in her voice. 'He's tough and experienced. He's a survivor. Besides, he won't be putting himself in any risky situations, especially not now that he's got you and Zoey to think about...'

Liv came round that evening, glowing with enthusiasm about her new relationship, gradually detecting the absence of a corresponding glow in Annie.

'You look like a ghost,' she teased Annie disapprovingly. They were having supper alfresco—chilled Frascati, French bread and cold chicken, on a checked cloth thrown over the wooden garden table. It was warm and muggy, the sky overcast, the roses starting to drop their petals in heaps all over the grass. 'Are you feeling okay, love?'

'I'm fine. Well, no, not exactly… I might as well tell you…' Annie drew a deep breath. 'I'm pregnant.'

'Anoushka!' Liv jumped from her seat, dark hair flying, and rushed to hug her. 'That's brilliant, absolutely wonderful, darling; aren't you pleased?'

Annie blinked away tears, hugged her sister in return, and then dug in her pocket for a tissue.

'Yes, of course…'

'What does Josh think he's up to, swanning off to Cambodia and leaving you to fret yourself into a Victorian decline?'

'Josh won't think I'm fretting,' Annie told her sister with bleak, desperate honesty. 'He thinks I hate him.'

Liv leaned back on her seat, crossed one jean-clad leg over the other, and stared at her in concern.

'Why would he think that?'

'It's a long story,' Annie confessed bitterly. 'I've made a real mess of this relationship, Livvy…' She drew a shaky breath, and pushed her plate away.

'Annie, darling—' Liv leaned forward, frowning '—you know what Josh said that night at Miles and Alison's? About how you were both wary of commitment, that Zoey brought you together…? Whatever else is going on in your marriage, it's obvious that Josh loves you very much, Annie…'

'No, you're wrong.'

'I'm not wrong; it's there in his voice, in his body language…'

Annie shook her head. 'He's just an accomplished performer. We both love Zoey. Josh doesn't love me. He doesn't even like me very much. He never has. He…fancies me. That's all. The whole thing was a set-up to save Zoey from her half-uncle. The trouble is, I love him; I love him so much I can't quite imagine life without him.'

'Why should you have to live without him?'

'He wants a divorce.'

'I don't believe it!'

'It was the last thing we talked about before he left.'

Liv was shaking her dark head, her eyes incredulous.

'You're telling me that, even knowing you're having his baby, Josh wants a divorce?'

'He doesn't know about the baby. But I'm not sure it will make much difference. He…he spoke as if my getting pregnant would be a problem, anyway. I think he's got something going with Veronica Whitton…'

'No way!' Liv protested staunchly. 'I asked Miles about her after that dinner at his and Alison's. He told me that Veronica and Josh used to be an item, but Josh finished it months ago. I'm sure as I can be there's nothing going on there, Annie…'

'Oh, Livvy…' She caught her breath, her voice tight with suppressed emotion. 'I'm going crazy; I must be to be so jealous. I hate him for how much he can hurt me! What if he's been abducted? Or…even killed…?'

'Before you can tell him how much you hate him, you mean? Yes, that would be tragic!' Liv's attempt at levity was bleak, but Annie found herself smiling reluctantly.

Liv poured more wine for herself and orange juice for Annie, and looked stern. 'He'll be back soon, in one piece, and you'll be able to sort this out,' she said firmly. 'Meanwhile, don't panic; think of your condition! Believe me, Josh will be back safe and sound before you know it.'

However, contrary to Liv's upbeat prediction, by the following lunchtime there was still no word from Josh, and Zoey had gone missing.

Annie had picked her up from the playgroup as usual, and left her playing in the safety of the back garden while she surreptitiously tried again to get through to Josh. This time, after much delay and help from the international operator, she made contact with someone who spoke English at the hotel in Siem Reap, but the woman there seemed dubious about anyone of that name having registered. She left an urgent message for him to ring her if he did appear, and put down the receiver, feeling far from reassured.

When she called Zoey in for lunch, she was nowhere to be found. She searched the big, rambling garden, expecting at any moment to see a glimpse of bright blue-bell-mauve dungarees and yellow T-shirt. She went round and round, checking in sheds and outhouses, calling, growing increasingly alarmed.

The side gate was firmly shut, but the bolt was undone. She opened the wooden gate and stared up and down the pavement outside, her heart beginning to thud uncomfortably. Could Zoey have got out here, run off somewhere? But surely she wouldn't have been able to turn the stiff knob, wrench open the heavy gate by herself. Could someone have come in here, taken Zoey away...? She went hot and cold, images of the half-uncle swimming into her mind. Had he let himself in here and abducted his niece?

'Oh, please, God, no,' Annie whispered, standing stock-still while her brain raced in crazy circles, imagining dreadful, unspeakable scenes. This couldn't happen to Zoey. She shut her eyes tightly and saw the image of Zoey's small, animated face, her tumbled black hair in bunches tied with yellow ribbons, her huge, haunted, dark eyes. The little girl had suffered enough traumas. If there was any justice in the world, this couldn't be happening...

Racing back to the house, she consulted Martha, searched every room, and then, in a cold sweat, she rang the police and rang Liv, who rang the rest of the family.

The remainder of the day was spent in a kind of vacuum of disbelief, punctuated only by the constant ringing of the telephone.

When the telephone rang for what seemed like the hundredth time, she snatched it up with a shaking hand. There was a long-distance crackle of static and then Josh's voice, sounding cool and husky and millions of miles away.

'Annie? How are things?'

She could hardly speak, suddenly, for the wave of anger that followed the brief, blinding joy that he was apparently safe and well.

'Where've you been?' she gabbled furiously, getting her breath back. 'You could have rung sooner, Josh. You were supposed to be home by now…!'

'Sorry, I couldn't ring; we had a spot of trouble on the Thai border. Is Zoey okay…?'

'Zoey's…oh, Josh, Zoey's missing.' She had to force herself to say the dreadful words. And then, for the first time since she'd embarked on the whole emotional rollercoaster of marrying Josh and taking on Zoey, she burst into uncontrollable tears.

'Annie…' After a brief, agonised silence, Josh's deep voice sounded strained, but suddenly gentle, communicating a robust common sense across the thousands of miles separating them. 'Sweetheart, it's okay, don't cry… Listen to me, Annie. Are you listening?'

'Yes…'

'Little children wander off all the time. Nearly always, no matter what you read in the newspapers, they come back safe and sound. Have you checked the house and garden? She could be hiding…'

'I've looked everywhere. I'm so afraid that someone's taken her, Josh…'

'Have you called the police?'

'Yes…'

'She's most likely hiding somewhere for a game,' he went on evenly. 'But get the police to check out the half-uncle's address, just to be on the safe side. And don't panic. He's a religious fanatic, but he's not a criminal. No actual harm will come to Zoey if he's taken her.'

Josh sounded so positive and calm, she felt some of her panic fading. Of course, he was right. Zoey would be fine. She'd reappear at any moment, and all the worry would have been for nothing.

'I'll be home tomorrow. Take care, Annie…'

'I wish you could get here sooner, Josh…'

'Me too.'

He rang off abruptly, but his last two words still rang in her ears, terse, hoarser than he'd sounded before. She felt such a void stretching between them that she cradled the receiver against her ear for a few moments longer, listening idiotically, as if the dialling tone somehow maintained the connection between them…

Once darkness fell, Zoey's absence seemed more poignant, more unbearable. The police checked the half-uncle's address and found no one home. They told Annie that they were 'trying to trace his whereabouts'. This seemed to make Zoey's abduction more definite. If the uncle wasn't home, presumably he'd taken Zoey and gone into hiding?

She couldn't sleep. Liv came for the night, and they sat up with Martha, drinking tea until the early hours, when Annie dozed off briefly in the chair by the phone. When she woke, she found that the other two had also fallen asleep in their chairs, the silence broken by Martha's gentle snoring and the birdsong outside in the garden. The early morning sun was creeping into the room.

'Even Blackie the cat's gone missing,' she told Liv over coffee later, bleakly ironic. 'Maybe it's me. Maybe I've offended the gods and this is my punishment.

Everything I care about shall be taken away from me, or something.'

'Oh, for heaven's sake,' Liv retorted robustly, 'don't start getting maudlin, Annie! How often does Blackie disappear for a night's mousing?'

'He hasn't come in for his supper,' she pointed out with a shrug. 'Anyway, I guess he might have gone back to my flat in Hampstead. I'll go round and check when…'

'When we've found Zoey,' Liv nodded, her gaze softening. 'Annie, darling, go and take a nice long bath and make yourself feel better. Please? You look absolutely all in…'

'You too,' Annie insisted stubbornly. 'And you, Martha. You've both sat up all night as well!'

In the end, they all went off to freshen up at the same time, availing themselves of Josh's generous quota of bathrooms, and Annie dragged the telephone in with her, so she could leap from the bath if it rang.

It did, and continued to do so throughout a tense and nerve-wracking day, but still there was no sign of Zoey.

Mid-afternoon, Liv and Martha sent Annie upstairs for a nap. She was exhausted but slept little.

A couple of hours later, dressed in fresh blue jeans, canvas pumps and white shirt, she went downstairs to the kitchen to find Josh walking in the back door, with a very pale, bedraggled Zoey in his arms.

Thumb in mouth, the little girl held out one arm to Annie, with a small, wary smile. Blackie had shot in in front of them, and was now crouched by his food dish, avidly devouring last night's rather jaded-looking supper.

'Don't ask,' Josh advised drily; he looked pale under his tan, shadows of fatigue under his eyes. His gaze moved with disturbing intensity over Annie as she stood, transfixed with shock and relief. 'Some milk and a sandwich, then a quick bath and bed is called for here; I'll sort that out if you like. I imagine you need to make some phone calls?'

'Right.' Taking his no-fuss cue, her heart swelling with relief, Annie smiled enquiringly into Zoey's face. 'Are you all right, poppet? We were all very worried about you…'

'Want Emile,' Zoey informed her sleepily, reaching out both arms now for Annie to take her. 'Want my teddy. Want Annie to put me to bed…'

'You've been out all night without Emile?' Annie quizzed her gently.

'I had Blackie with me,' Zoey explained, nestling her head against Annie's neck. The child's eyes closed. She fell asleep almost instantly, a dead weight in her arms.

Josh stood there, watching, his face unreadable. In crumpled khaki trousers and a fawn cotton shirt he looked haggard, travel-weary, but nevertheless stunningly attractive, Annie registered with a pang. She met his eyes over Zoey's small, tousled head, and he made a wry face.

'She was frightened I was going to die, like Max,' he murmured bleakly. 'She didn't want to hear the worst, apparently, so she was hiding in the loft over the garage until I got back…'

'Hiding…?'

'Similar to the ostrich and sand principle, I guess. I got out of the car and she appeared down the ladder, clutching the cat…'

Annie blinked away tears, and turned to take Zoey upstairs. The food and the warm bath could wait, she decided, gazing at the small, sleeping face as she tucked the child into bed. She made do with a quick wipe over her face and grubby hands with a flannel, and a gentle brush to de-tangle the wild black hair. Sending up another silent prayer of thanks, she then left her sleeping soundly, with the door ajar, and went downstairs again.

By the time everyone knew of the happy outcome, and Josh had disappeared for a reviving shower and change after his journey, another hour had gone by.

Finally, with Liv gone and Martha busy in the kitchen, Annie found herself alone with Josh, with very mixed feelings. A tray of tea and sandwiches sat between them on the sun-dappled table in the conservatory. Josh, in jeans and a checked shirt, looked so large and male and reassuring, she almost found herself forgetting the chasm between them. Even the nightmare of the long night and day just passed seemed unreal.

'You look exhausted,' he commented, eyeing her over the rim of his cup. 'You must have had a rough time.'

'You could say that. You don't look terribly bright yourself.'

'I don't normally sleep too badly on planes. But once I knew Zoey was missing I guess sleep didn't come easily. I confess I immediately thought her half-uncle was behind it.'

'I can't believe she was hiding in the garage loft all this time.' She shook her head slowly. 'I had a quick look up there. And I called and called, everywhere. I blame myself. She obviously overheard my frantic telephone calls, trying to get in touch with you...'

'You were trying to contact me before she went missing?'

She felt herself going hotter, under that enquiring gaze.

'Well, yes. Zoey wasn't the only one worried you might get killed like Max,' she confessed quietly. 'I'd been trying to ring you for ages...'

'I'm touched,' he said, a hint of irony in his voice.

She felt herself getting angry again.

'There's no need to be sarcastic,' she said shortly.

'Anyone would have been worried when you didn't come back on time. Cambodia was on the news a lot...'

'I'm sorry you were worried, Annie.' he said seriously. 'So...you just wanted to check I was all right?'

'Yes...'

'Nothing else?'

'Well...' She met his eyes, and felt a jolt of awareness. He knew. He must know... 'As a matter of fact,' she continued awkwardly, her stomach feeling decidedly hollow, 'there was something else...'

'Yes, Annie?'

She stood up abruptly and walked to the French doors. She stood with her back to him, her arms hugging her body.

'You remember your display of...of masculine intuition before you left?' she said, her voice small and formal. 'Unfortunately, I was wrong and you were right...'

There was an electric silence when she stopped speaking.

'You are pregnant.' Josh's voice, when he spoke at last, was hard to decipher.

'Yes...'

'What the hell took you so long to find out?' he demanded huskily. 'Surely all the signs must have been there, Annie?'

She felt herself going hot. 'I didn't miss a period. My...my doctor said that happens sometimes. It doesn't mean there's anything wrong. Anyway, I did a home test, and then he confirmed the result. I'm definitely pregnant. But it doesn't make any difference, Josh. If we can't make our relationship work for Zoey, it's unlikely to work any better for a new baby. So I agree with you— if...if you want a divorce, we'd better make it sooner rather than later. That would be kinder for everyone...'

'Annie...' He was behind her, taking hold of her shoulders, his grip none too gentle as he twisted her round to face him. 'Let me get this straight. You're telling me that you're expecting my baby...our baby...but you want a divorce?'

She stared up at him, trembling.

'You're the one who wants a divorce,' she said huskily. 'You said—'

'Annie!' His growl of reaction sent her nervous system into fresh spirals of panic. 'I do not want a divorce! Do you understand?'

She stared at him in stunned silence. Through the haze of emotion, confused anger crept back.

'Oh, I see,' she whispered bitterly. 'I've triggered off the ''proud father'' streak now, haven't I? You want me to stay married to you because I'm carrying your baby. Suddenly I'm worth hanging onto. That's it, isn't it, Josh?'

He let go of her shoulders slowly. His dark face was like a mask. He was breathing unevenly, the muscles of his chest jerking beneath his shirt.

'Is that what you really think of me?' he said hoarsely. 'Is it, Annie?'

'What else am I to think?' She reacted like an automaton. 'Before you left for your research trip, you asked me if I was pregnant, implied that it would be a problem if I was, and—'

'A problem to you, not me!' he cut in roughly. 'Annie, you've been treating me like a leper since our wedding day! When I suspected you were pregnant, I wasn't sure how you might be feeling...how much you'd want to have my baby...' Raking a hand through his black hair, he fixed her with a gaze so rapier-like, she felt physically pinned to the ground. 'God help me, Annie, how did I end up in such an unholy mess?'

'Best of intentions backfiring, I suppose,' she said as calmly as she could. 'You saw that Zoey needed emergency measures, you asked me, and the situation got out of hand…'

'I'm not talking about that.' He thrust both hands through his now tousled hair, then clutched the back of his neck as if trying to ease unbearable tension. 'I'm talking about you and me! About my…crass, inept, bloody useless handling of the one relationship in my life that means everything to me.'

She stared at him blankly.

'I don't understand.'

He gave a short, self-mocking laugh. He dropped his hands to his sides, thrust them into the pockets of his jeans.

'Don't you, Annie? Okay, it's probably too late; you won't believe me, but let me run this by you anyway. I'm a coward; I love you, but I've never found the courage to admit it. I wasn't play-acting that night at Miles's house, Annie. I was announcing the truth in front of everyone. That way, if you rejected me at least I could claim I was keeping up appearances. I could hang onto my pride.'

His wide mouth twisted bitterly at the frozen silence which followed. He took his hands out of his pockets and folded his arms across his chest.

'Impressed?' he quipped, his voice raw. 'I thought you would be. Don't tell me you never suspected how I felt about you. Why do you think I erupted in that jealous rage over Phoenix? Why do you think I pursued you with such persistence after Miles's wedding? Why do you think I flipped over Derrick Butterford?'

'Josh…' She found her voice at last, cleared her throat. 'Josh, if you love someone, you trust them…'

'Not if you're fairly sure they don't love you in return, Annie,' he corrected her bleakly. 'Then trust seems too dangerous to risk. Trusting someone just gives them ten times the power to hurt you.'

She felt herself going hot and cold with emotion.

'Yes,' she said chokingly, 'you're right... I should know.'

There was a taut, charged silence.

'Why, Annie?' Josh's voice was careful. 'Why would you know?'

'Because...I haven't exactly trusted you, since I've known you,' she explained simply, her voice husky with nerves. 'Even though...' She stopped, taking a deep breath before she found the courage to finish. 'Even though I've loved you since that summer in Greece two years ago.'

Her heart was thumping against her ribs.

Josh had unfolded his arms. He was gazing at her so intently, she felt mesmerised. The air seemed to have been sucked out of the space around them. Even the invisible molecules in that space seemed to be vibrating with electricity.

'Are you telling the truth, Annie?'

'Why would I lie?' She managed a quick, tense smile.

'Will you believe me if I tell you that I fell in love with you that day you cut your foot in the sea?' The dark gaze above hers was bright and hard.

'Um...maybe. You haven't exactly spent the last two years trying to convince me, have you?'

'If you'll let me, I promise to spend the next few decades trying to convince you. Will that do?'

She could only stare at him idiotically as the impact of his words slowly sank in. Then she caught a shuddering breath.

'Josh, is it true?' she whispered fiercely. 'Do you love me? Really?'

'Really,' he assured her unevenly, pulling her close; a breathtaking gleam in his eyes conveying far more confidence than the words which followed. 'Now, tell me the truth, Annie, darling; do you think you could eventually manage to forgive me for being a suspicious, cynical bastard? Given time, and lots of TLC, and offers of nappy-changing from a prospective new father?'

She caught her breath again jerkily.

'Josh, speaking of…of being suspicious and cynical, how do I know you're not just saying you love me because…because I'm expecting your baby, and you feel obliged…?'

Guiding her back to the table, he pushed her down gently into a chair. Drawing another chair closer, he sat down opposite her and took both her hands in his. His face was tense.

'Annie, listen. You have to believe me. All my adult life I've kept my distance in relationships…'

'Why?' she prompted softly, when he stopped. 'Because of what happened when you were a child, Josh? Because of your mother?'

'I guess so…' He gave her a hunted look, his smile self-mocking. 'It's hard trusting people not to hurt you when deep down you're still angry with the one person who's supposed never to hurt you…'

'I can see that,' she whispered, tightening her hands around his, her throat swelling. 'I understand that part, Josh. I must confess I'd like to throttle my new mother-in-law and I've never even met her!'

Josh shook his head, smiling bleakly.

'She's charming. You'll like her. I get along okay with her these days, Annie. But until I met you it didn't seem to matter too much whether I trusted a woman enough to risk a lasting relationship.'

He gave her a wry, searing look. 'When I met you my instincts told me you were different. But every damn thing seemed to conspire to convince me you were just like I imagined all the others to be. Then when I was away in Cambodia…' He stopped, his expression grim. 'Well, let's say a couple of incidents over there reminded me, as if I needed it, of just how short life is. I resolved then that when I got home I'd rip up that cold, artificial contract of marriage we had drawn up and risk being honest with you...'

'I felt the same way.' She blinked back tears. 'When I knew I was having our baby, I was so happy, Josh, and then I was so confused. I couldn't wait to talk to you, even though I wasn't sure what your reaction would be, and when I couldn't get hold of you I nearly went mad, imagining the awful things that could have happened...'

'I pictured you glad to see the back of me for a few days,' he admitted hoarsely. 'Annie, I missed you so much, I couldn't wait for the return flight...'

She bit her lip, unable to stop herself from asking quietly, 'What should I know about Veronica?'

Josh's eyes darkened.

'There's very little to know. Veronica and I had a casual thing going last year. It was all over several months ago. She's one of those women who find it hard to accept no for an answer. I swear to you I only dropped in to that drinks party of hers for an hour because my agent told me he'd be there and he was going on holiday the next day.'

'She told me you stayed on ages after everyone else...'

'Talking to Jack, my agent,' Josh said gently. 'In fact, Jack and I left together and went for a drink. You can call him to check if you like.'

She shuddered, shaking her head.

'No, I don't think I need do that, Josh. I believe you.'

'Thank you.' His eyes were wry. 'I'm glad. Because that's the truth, Annie. While we're on the subject of past relationships, can we talk about Derrick Butterford?'

Annie blushed slightly.

'You mean his behaviour at our wedding reception? He was just muck-stirring, Josh; he must have hung around and waited for his moment to cause you maximum offence. Wounded pride, I gather, from the brief conversation I had in the course of changing my accountants! We only had a few friendly dinner dates and theatre trips…' She felt herself going even hotter at the kindling, possessive gleam in Josh's eyes. 'I…I had no idea he'd react so vindictively when he heard I was getting married.'

'I can see he's the jealous type. And it takes one to know one.' He grinned faintly, the warmth in his eyes making her feel dizzy with joy. 'Have you told Zoey, by the way? About the baby?'

She slowly shook her head. She was quietly revelling in the luxury of Josh's warm, strong hands enclosing hers. Her heart felt as if it might burst with emotion…

'Not yet, but she's been talking about a friend at the play group whose mother's expecting a new baby, so that'll make it easier…'

'It might help her to settle down completely, accept us as her new parents, make her feel part of a real family,' Josh said seriously, frowning slightly. 'What do you think?'

Annie felt her smile widen to an idiotic grin of happiness.

'I think you are the nicest person I know,' she said simply.

'As cowards go?'

'You're not a coward, Josh,' she said shakily. 'And, anyway, you could use the same description for me. If I'd been braver I'd have risked telling you I loved you right at the start…'

He slowly stood up and reached to pull her up in front of him. Annie lifted her hands and with shy hunger traced the hard bones of his face with her fingers, the need to touch him and caress him so powerful she was trembling with impatience.

With a shudder, Josh crushed her even closer, so that they were moulded from breast to thigh. Her whole body reacted dramatically to the contact of the hard male body against hers. She wrapped her arms round his neck and clutched him tighter.

'As well as missing you like hell,' he went on huskily, 'and hating myself for alienating you, I've been torturing myself with fantasies of making love to you again…'

'Have you?' she managed weakly; her legs felt boneless, she was melting into the power of his body. 'What sort of fantasies?'

'Just say you love me again, and I'll show you.'

'I love you,' she whispered, a wash of colour flooding her face and then fading, leaving her white with tension, gripped suddenly with apprehension even as the words released weeks of pent-up emotions. 'I love you, Josh…'

She found herself scooped triumphantly into his arms and carried upstairs. In the large bedroom where she'd slept alone since their wedding day, he placed her almost reverently on the bed and went to lock the door.

'Wait…' She felt hot all over with a mixture of desire and shyness. 'We can't…not right now, Josh… What if Zoey wakes up?'

'It's okay; Martha promised to keep an ear out for Zoey,' he said huskily. 'I told her I needed some time alone with you, to sort things out…'

Annie went even hotter.

'Annie…' he breathed, sitting down beside her, his eyes focused on her wide gaze. 'Darling, you're so beautiful, so sexy…if you knew how I've wanted you these last few weeks…' He dropped a slow, possessive kiss on her lips and slid his hands beneath the hem of her shirt, burning a path of awareness as he stroked hungrily over her bare midriff. Then he stopped, his eyes dark with sudden concern as he searched her face. 'Is it okay, though? Did the doctor say that making love was safe, sweetheart…?'

'Yes…' Her laugh was shy but fierce as she stared up at Josh's dark, intense expression. 'I didn't actually ask him, because…well, with the way things were between us, that was the last thing on my mind…but he gave me the information anyway! Said my husband and I could continue to enjoy a normal sex life.'

'There's something else I need to know, Annie…' He was unfastening the buttons on her shirt with hands which shook slightly. 'In fact, there are two very important things I have to ask you…'

He was pulling her shirt off, pausing to shrug his own shirt over his head before tossing them both to the floor. He crushed her close, overwhelming her with the sensation of warm, male body against her own soft curves.

'Ask me, then,' she said, wriggling to look into his face, her whole body tingling with impatience for his touch.

'First of all…' he propped himself on his elbow and took her chin in his thumb and forefinger to scan her hot face '…tell me why you stayed a virgin for so long, Annie.'

'Oh…!' Her throat dried abruptly. She blinked up at him. 'I just didn't meet anyone I wanted to make love with,' she managed huskily, 'until I met you…'

His expression grew more intense.

'So…what about that night in your flat, Annie, when you stopped me?'

'I was terrified. I'd loved you since that summer in Greece. I wanted to make love with you, but with all the suspicion between us, Josh, I just…just lost my nerve…'

'Okay. Second question,' he said hoarsely. 'When I barged in here on our wedding day, and accused you of sleeping with Derrick, and then made love to you think

ing you were experienced…hell, sweetheart, that was no
way to lose your virginity. I've been cursing my stupidity ever since. Did I put you off sex, darling? Tell me
the truth. I'll wait if you want me to wait. I'll take things
easy. I'll do anything I can to put things right…'

She started to shake with guilty laughter as every
nerve in her body sparked into magical life at his touch.

'Josh, stop it. Stop feeling guilty. You're making me
feel guilty…'

'I couldn't live with myself if I thought our baby was
conceived in bitterness, Annie, darling…'

'No, our baby was conceived in…bliss, and temporary
misunderstanding,' she advised him breathlessly, her
eyes flaring with happiness. 'Now I think we should re-
write that marriage contract, Josh…'

'We'll burn it,' he told her, with a gleam in his eyes
that took her breath away. 'We didn't even have a honeymoon, sweetheart…'

'I don't need one, now I know you love me…'

'We could go back to Skiathos, soon…' he murmured,
kissing her with mounting hunger. 'Would you like
that?'

'Mmm…that might be nice. We have to think about
Zoey, though…she's still really insecure…' She wriggled in the warmth of his arms, stroking the firm muscles
of his back with delicate impatience. Her breathing grew
ragged as he unclipped her lacy white bra and devoured
her with his eyes before kissing the exposed silky flesh
with tantalising slowness.

'We could take Zoey with us,' Josh went on softly.
'Sophia would baby-sit…'

'That's a lovely idea, Josh…but right now all I can
think about is how much I want you to make love to
me…' she whispered achingly.

'You mean that?' There was such breathtaking ardour
in his heavy-lidded gaze, she felt her heart swell.

'Of course I do. I feel ashamed of the way I acted after...after you made love to me that first time.' She smiled slightly, sliding her fingers into his hair. 'You didn't act like a sex-crazed animal at all, Josh...'

He groaned, his eyes warm on her flushed face.

'I didn't?'

'No, you were wonderful. It was wonderful. That's the truth. Not the suspicious, jealous bit beforehand, of course...and not the tiny bit that hurt...and not being accused of getting my revenge on you afterwards...'

'Oh, God, Annie...'

'But the bit where you made me feel like...like I was going up in flames, like I was going to die of pleasure. The way you made me feel...I've never felt anything like that before, in my whole life, and...' She faltered, finishing up in a small, tenderly teasing voice, 'And if possible I'd very much like to experience it again...'

Dark colour surged along Josh's cheekbones as he dropped a triumphant kiss on her lips. He smiled down into her melting brown eyes. He moved lower to unbutton her jeans and trail warm, hungry, seeking kisses over the smooth plane of her stomach, making her shiver and writhe with delight.

'Please, Josh?'

'I'll see what I can do,' he said, with a grin.

MILLS & BOON®

Next Month's Romances

♡

Each month you can choose from a wide variety of romance novels from Mills & Boon. Below are the new titles to look out for next month from the Presents™ and Enchanted™ series.

Presents™

A NANNY FOR CHRISTMAS	Sara Craven
A FORBIDDEN DESIRE	Robyn Donald
THE WINTER BRIDE	Lynne Graham
THE PERFECT MATCH?	Penny Jordan
RED-HOT AND RECKLESS	Miranda Lee
BARGAIN WITH THE WIND	Kathleen O'Brien
THE DISOBEDIENT BRIDE	Elizabeth Power
ALL MALE	Kay Thorpe

Enchanted™

SANTA'S SPECIAL DELIVERY	Val Daniels
THE MARRIAGE PACT	Elizabeth Duke
A MIRACLE FOR CHRISTMAS	Grace Green
ACCIDENTAL WIFE	Day Leclaire
ONE NIGHT BEFORE CHRISTMAS	Catherine Leigh
A SINGULAR HONEYMOON	Leigh Michaels
A HUSBAND FOR CHRISTMAS	Emma Richmond
TEMPORARY GIRLFRIEND	Jessica Steele

Jennifer
BLAKE

GARDEN
of
SCANDAL

She wants her life back...

Branded a murderer, Laurel Bancroft has
been a recluse for years. Now she wants her
life back—but someone in her past will do
anything to ensure the truth stays buried.

*"Blake's style is as steamy as a still July
night...as overwhelmingly hot as Cajun spice."*
—Chicago Tribune

AVAILABLE IN PAPERBACK
FROM NOVEMBER 1997

GET TO KNOW

THE BEST OF ENEMIES

the latest blockbuster from TAYLOR SMITH

Who would you trust with your life? Think again.

*Linked to a terrorist bombing, a young student goes
missing. One woman believes in the girl's innocence
and is determined to find her before she is silenced.
Leya Nash has to decide—quickly—who to trust.
The wrong choice could be fatal.*

Valid only in the UK & Ireland against purchases made in retail outlets
and not in conjunction with any Reader Service or other offer.

- -

50ᵖ OFF
COUPON
VALID UNTIL: 28.2.1998
TAYLOR SMITH'S *THE BEST OF ENEMIES*

To the Customer: This coupon can be used in part payment for a
copy of Taylor Smith's THE BEST OF ENEMIES. Only one coupon can
be used against each copy purchased. Valid only in the UK & Ireland
against purchases made in retail outlets and not in conjunction with
any Reader Service or other offer. Please do not attempt to redeem
this coupon against any other product as refusal to accept may cause
embarrassment and delay at the checkout.

To the Retailer: Harlequin Mills & Boon will redeem this coupon at
face value provided only that it has been taken in part payment for a
copy of Taylor Smith's THE BEST OF ENEMIES. The company reserves
the right to refuse payment against misredeemed coupons. Please
submit coupons to: Harlequin Mills & Boon Ltd. NCH Dept 730,
Corby, Northants NN17 1NN.

9 904170 200509

0472 00189